THE TREASURE HOUSE OF EASTERN
STORY UNDER THE DIRECTORSHIP
OF
SIR E. DENISON ROSS

HITOPADEŚA

A Book of Wholesome Counsel

A Translation from the original Sanskrit
by Francis Johnson: revised and in part
re-written with an introduction by Lionel
D. Barnett, M.A., Litt.D.

STORIES FROM SA'DÍ'S BUSTÁN
AND GULISTÁN

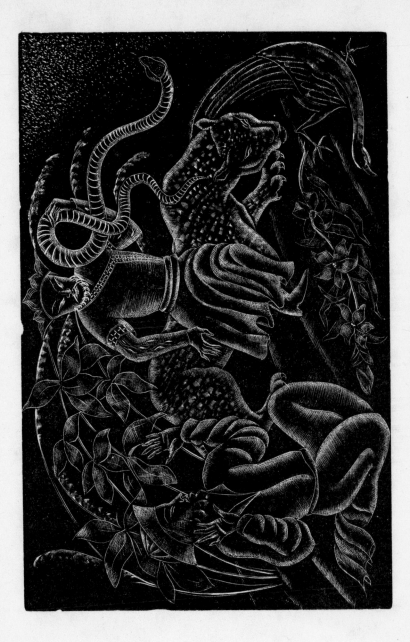

STORIES FROM THE *BUSTÁN* OF SHAYKH SA'DÍ TOGETHER WITH SELECTIONS FROM FRANCIS GLADWIN'S TRANSLATION OF SA'DÍ'S *GULISTÁN*, THE FORMER TRANSLATED AND THE LATTER REVISED BY REUBEN LEVY, M.A., LECTURER IN PERSIAN IN THE UNIVERSITY OF CAMBRIDGE

WITH A FRONTISPIECE
BY
CYNTHIA KENT

NEW YORK
FREDERICK A. STOKES COMPANY
PUBLISHERS

Printed in Great Britain at
The Westminster Press, London, W. 9
and bound by
A. W. Bain & Co. Ltd.

For the benefit of students and others interested references to the original Persian are given in the footnotes. The editions used are, for the *Bustan*, that of C. H. Graf, Vienna, 1858; for the *Gulistán*, that of J. Platts.

Since this work is mainly concerned with Sa'dí's stories, much of his moralising, some of it tedious, has been omitted in the *Bustan* translation.

b

NOTE

*Passages in the Gulistán marked by single inverted
commas are in verse in the original
An accent over a vowel denotes that it is long.*

INTRODUCTION

S O M E little time before Saladin captured Jerusalem from the Crusaders, there was born in
distant Shiraz a person destined to suffer in the
subsequent struggle to regain the holy city. He
was Sa'dí, Musharrifu 'l-Dín or Muslihu 'l-Dín ibn
'Abdullah—both the former being honorific
titles, for his real name is unknown—a poet whose
work is as familiar in Persia as the Koran itself,
and is better appreciated. Tradition says that he
was born in A.D. 1184, three years before Saladin's
victory, and that he died at the age of 110
lunar years in A.D. 1291, but neither date rests on
certain authority, though the adventures with
which Sa'dí's career was crammed might well
demand a longer life than the average to have
contained them all.

At the time when the poet was born, history
was being made, not only in Western Asia, but
further east. The Muslim triumph coincided with
the beginnings of a temporary revival of the
Caliphate at Baghdad, where the Caliph al-Násir
was again asserting the ancient authority of his
office in the face of the Seljúq Sultans, potentates
whose powers were now crumbling before the
onslaughts of their rivals, the princes of Khwá-
razm (Khiva). In Central Asia there were the first
tribal stirrings which threw up Chingiz Khan,

" The Scourge of God," and were to send waves
of bloodthirsty Mongol warriors east to the China
Sea, west to the Danube, and south almost to the
Persian Gulf.

At Shiraz, Sa'dí's birthplace, there ruled as
vassals of the Khwárazm-Sháhs a family of Atá-
begs whose founder had been chamberlain to the
Seljúq Sultan Tughril Beg. One of the Atábeg
dynasty, Sa'd ibn Zangí, who came to the throne
in A.D. 1195, took an interest in the family of the
poet, who later on honoured his patron by adopt-
ing the *takhallus*, or pen-name, of Sa'dí. When,
at an early age, Sa'dí lost his father, who had been
in the service of the royal household, the prince
undertook to complete the education which the
future poet had begun in tender years. He sent
the lad to Baghdad to study at the famous Nizámíya *madrasa* or College, which had been founded
by Nizámu 'l Mulk, the Seljúq vizier whom
legend connects fictitiously with Omat Khayyam
and the Old Man of the Mountains.

Sa'dí seems to have impressed the College
authorities with his ability, and he was appointed
to be a *répétiteur* or lecturer. He tells us in the
Bustan that he well deserved the emoluments he
was given, being kept busy day and night—somewhat like Charles Lamb's schoolmaster—in a
perpetual cycle of teaching and repetitions. Even
so he found time for outside interests. He made
the acquaintance of the Sufi ascetic Shaykh 'Umar

Suhrawardí who initiated him into the mysteries of Sufiism and taught him what asceticism meant. So deep was the older man's influence that throughout his long life, on his many journeyings, Sa'dí was able without arousing suspicion to adopt the character and the garb of the dervish, with its staff and patched cloak and begging bowl. Many of his stories tell of this wandering life of hardship, during which he made the acquaintance of the queer characters that are to be met with on almost any page of the *Bustan* and *Gulistán*.

In spite of his preoccupation at Baghdad with the sterner aspects of mysticism, Sa'dí's joy in life would not be denied expression, and displayed itself in many lyrics filled with his rapturous delight in the beauty and desirability of the world, coupled with warnings of its transience and the need for making the most of it before the " drum for departure " was sounded. The fame of his poetry spread abroad while he was still attached to the Nizamíya, and when in A.D. 1210 he attached himself to a trading caravan and went to Kashgar in Turkestan on the confines of China, he found that he and his work were known there.

The journey to Kashgar was not the only one that Sa'dí made from Baghdad. It was from there he took the opportunity of making his first pilgrimage to Mecca, and it is possible also that he visited Damascus. According to the biographer Dawlatsháh, Sa'dí pursued his studies for thirty

years. As a rough generalisation the statement
will stand, and what may be called the poet's
specifically academic career did not come to an
end until A.D. 1226, when his patron Sa'd ibn
Zangí was succeeded by Abu Bakr his son. By
that time Sa'dí had been back in Shiraz for some
years, though he had been kept away much longer
than he wished by the activities of Chingiz Khan's
hordes and by internal disturbances in Fars, due
to the Atábeg Abu Bakr's usurpation of his father's
throne. On the accession of Abu Bakr, the poet
left Shiraz, for some reason that is not quite clear.
It may be that the old patronage was not continued to him—and in fact in one of his odes he
says:

"My soul is weary of Shiraz, utterly sick and sad;
　If you seek for news of my doings, you will have
　　　to ask at Baghdad.
Sa'dí, that love of one's native land is a true
　　　tradition is clear!
But I cannot afford to die of want because my
　　　birth was here."*

Yet it is equally possible that the restless disposition which made him frequently expatiate on
the advantages of travel about the world—advantages which he had himself discovered even as a
student—drove him to a life of wandering. Whatever the reason for his going, his travels in the

* E. G. Browne: *Literary History of Persia*. Vol. II, p.
536.

next period of his life took him very far afield, if
we are to judge from the references in the *Bustan*
and the *Gulistán*, both of which he wrote at an
advanced age. It was apparently during this period
of travel, which Dawlatsháh puts at thirty years,
that he was captured by the Franks, probably by a
raiding party of Crusaders from Tripoli. He was
first put to work in the moat at Tripoli with other
miserable wretches, but had the good fortune to
be recognised by an important citizen of Aleppo
with whom he had acquaintance, and who happened to see him at his labours. The sum of ten
dinars ransomed him from the infidels, and after
their return to Aleppo his rescuer offered him a
dowry of a hundred dinars to marry his daughter.
Sa'dí consented, but his married life does not
appear to have been a very happy one. With considerable humour, in a story in the Gulistán* he
describes a quarrel he had with his wife, who
seems to have accused him of ingratitude.

" Did not my father buy you out for ten
dinars? " she cried.

" Yes," he answers, " he released me from
Frankish chains for ten dinars, but for a hundred
dinars he made me a prisoner to you."

Sa'dí does not say whether he took his wife
with him when he set off again, but he hints at
another marriage or at least a liaison in San'á in
Arabia, presumably on his way to the Persian

* II, 31.

Gulf and so to India. It was on the island of Kísh (Qays), the trade centre of the Gulf in Sa'dí's day, that he met a rich and restless merchant who could not make up his mind what his next objective was to be. He confided to the poet that after one journey more he could retire and spend the rest of his days quietly in his shop. It was to be a long journey. He could carry sulphur from his native Fars to China, from there he would export porcelain to Byzantium, thence he would take Greek brocades to India and return to Aleppo with Indian steel. From Aleppo he would carry glass to Yemen in Arabia and return home to Fars with Yemenite cloth. The narrative fires the imagination, and by showing what intercommunication was possible in the Orient in the thirteenth century of our era, it answers one of the doubts which have been cast upon Sa'dí's accounts of his adventures, notably in the Hindu temple of Somnáth.

In the *Bustan* the poet describes how he found himself in the temple in Kathiawar on the shores of the Indian Ocean. There, in the presence of a bejewelled idol which raises its hands heavenward at times of prayer, he makes some contemptuous remark which brings him under the suspicious eyes of the Brahmans. Only the pretence that he is a recent arrival, unacquainted with the significance of the image, and of the faith of which its worship is the centre, saves him from destruction by the angry worshippers. He is made to remain the whole of one night in the temple so that a demonstration from the idol in the morning will convince him of the virtue of belief in it. Somehow or other he manages to find his way behind the scenes where he finds a priest holding in his hands a cord which obviously moves the idol's arms. Seeing that the secret has been found out, the priest leaps upon Sa'dí, who grapples with him and throws him down a well.

Absurd errors, such as the confusion of Brahmans with " fire-worshippers " are not lacking in the story, and it is possible that Sa'dí sees himself in the rôle of hero in some story which he has heard; or it may be merely that he has embroidered some incident which actually occurred. There is no reason on that account to deny, as some have done, that he went to India, where he seems to have visited both the Punjab and Gujerat.

The references in the *Bustan* and the *Gulistán* indicate that at some period of his career he also visited North Africa and Egypt as well as Asia Minor, in addition to making several more pilgrimages to Mecca. It is not clear whether he visited Africa before his voyage to India or as an extension of one of his journeys to Mecca; at any rate there were periods in between when he returned to Persia and lived at Isfahan.

In the fateful years when the second wave of Mongols under Húlágú Khan were sweeping over the lands of the Eastern Caliphate towards Baghdad

which it ultimately destroyed in A.D. 1258, Saʻdí
was seized by a home-sickness that drove him
back to his native place. Its reigning prince, Abu
Bakr, had declared his allegiance to the Mongol
conquerors and his province and capital were
consequently left in comparative peace. At Shiraz,
which he appears to have reached in A.D. 1255,
the poet settled in a secluded spot outside the city,
and impelled by the thought of what he considered
a wasted life, he began a race against the day when
his "caravan" should start "for the dawn of
nothing." If it is true that he died in A.D. 1291,
the day was delayed for thirty-five years, the most
fruitful period of his long career, during which
time he was able to set down the thoughts that had
been suggested to him in the course of his extended
and adventurous life.

Saʻdí was an old man when he wrote most of
his works. The fiery enthusiasms of youth had
been tempered by his years of varied experience,
and it is the product of his ripe wisdom that he
presents to his readers in the *Bustan* and *Gulistán*,
works with which his name is universally associated, though he was a prolific writer in all forms
of verse. It will be seen from these two books that
he propounded a practical and worldly philosophy
based upon expediency, and that he was a stranger
to metaphysics. He delighted to preach what are
ordinarily called the Christian virtues: humility,
charity, gentleness and the like; but he was no

ascetic, and he made no attempt to deter others from the earthly delights which he had so obviously himself enjoyed.

The *Bustan*, which was completed in A.D. 1257 contains within its ten sections of facile and often beautiful verse, dissertations on justice, good government, beneficence, earthly and mystic love, humility, submissiveness, contentment and other excellences. The *Gulistán*, which seems to be a kind of supplement to the other work, is made up of mixed prose and verse and covers practically the same ground. It is a lighter and more humorous compilation than the *Bustan* and, like it, contains numerous anecdotes, taken very often from the author's own accumulated experiences, to illustrate the practice of the virtues by famous personages, warriors and saints, kings and courtiers.

It must be borne in mind when the stories are being read that to Sa'dí the important point in each was the moral, and he proves himself an excellent preacher—or perhaps we ought rather to say " showman "—by his ability to arouse our interest at the beginning with the promise of an adventure and leading us on, almost without knowing it, to the lesson at the end. The ethical character of that teaching is not always beyond question, as for example in the first story from the *Gulistán*, where the moral is that " a lie which makes up good will is better than a truth that stirs up mischief." But most of the time the poet crowns true virtue with his praise and he delights in picturing the ideal of ethical conduct. Much indeed may be forgiven him for the charming simplicity of his stories, and in his presentation of easily assimilated wisdom there is a freshness that makes it palatable even to those who have not acquired the Oriental taste for established truths—or what we call platitudes.

Dawlatsháh calls Sa'dí's work "the salt-cellar of the poets" into which all dip for the seasoning of their own concoctions. Rarely indeed are his stories lacking in wit or the touch of irony which is, perhaps, the best appreciated of all literary seasonings. It is by them that he makes up for an occasional deficiency of the poetic justice which we demand from a satisfactory story, although the numerous translations of the *Bustan* and *Gulistán* into all modern literatures prove that there are tales enough in them which satisfy Western taste. In criticism it must be said that the poet has not always the art to let well alone and will spoil an excellent story which points its own moral by dragging in a didactic tag which comes as absolute bathos upon the rest. But then, it must be repeated, to him the real point of the story was its moral.

Of Sa'dí's other work this is not the place to speak at length. Some of his odes have been considered as good as any produced by Hafiz of

Shiraz, the greatest of all Persian lyricists, and if that estimate does not apply to all of his poems, their occasional excellence cannot be questioned. The poet's dependence on the goodwill of princely patrons accounts for the number of his *qasidas* or panegyric poems both in Persian and Arabic, and also probably for a collection of *mutayabát* (jests) otherwise known as *khabíthát* (obscene poems). The latter name best indicates the character of the collection, which the author justified on the ground that princes must be kept amused, and in the fashion which best accords with their desires, though it was only with reluctance that he undertook the task. It speaks well for the poet that his name lives by his more edifying ethical works and that the veneration which they called forth in his own lifetime earned him the title of " Shaykh Sa'dí," or simply " Shaykh," by which the Muslim world knows him to this day.

THE BUSTAN
or
SCENTED GARDEN

ON JUSTICE, EQUITY AND
GOOD GOVERNMENT

A M O N G S T the traditions of the mighty ones
of the Faith who truly knew the inner verities
is the story that once a man of piety bestrode a
leopard which he drove along with a serpent.
" O traveller on God's way," said a man to him,
" be my guide on the path you have taken. How
did you contrive to bend this ravening beast to
your will and to have the bezel of fortune's ring
inscribed with your name? " He replied: " You
need not marvel that leopards and serpents or
even elephants and vultures are obedient to me.
Only refrain from shirking God's command and
no one will ever shirk yours."*

From the ocean of Oman there once landed a
voyager who had travelled far by land and sea.
He had seen Arab and Turk, Tajik and Greek,
and his pious soul was filled with learning in
every branch. He had gone about the world
gathering knowledge, and on his travels had
learnt all that intercourse with men could teach.

* Graf's edition, p. 21.

I   B

In body he was strong as a sound oak, yet he was utterly destitute and bereft of means. Two hundred patches formed his cloak, and his soul was scorched in the fire of hardship. On the seashore he came to a city whose ruler, a prince with great regard for pious fame, laid his head in humility at the holy dervish's feet. In the baths the royal servants washed away the dust of travel from his head and body. In obeisance, then, he laid his head on the king's threshold, spoke his praises hand on breast, then entered the royal halls, saying, " May your fortune flourish and may fate be your servant." The king asked him whence he came and how it was he reached that kingdom, and, further, what he had seen in it of good or ill. " Tell me that," said he, " O possessor of goodly fame and of all good qualities."

" Lord of the world," he replied, " May God be your helper and fortune your associate. Not a single stage have I travelled in this country where I have seen a heart in grief through oppression. It is sufficient majesty and glory for a king that he will not approve of hurt to any man. I have seen no one's head heavy with wine and the taverns are in ruins."

Thus he embroidered the skirt of speech with pearls, so skilfully that the king raised his arms in amazement. The fellow's eloquent words delighted him; he summoned him to his side and did him honour, giving him gold and jewels

2

in gratitude for his coming and enquiring about his stock and native land. To the king's questions he replied, telling of his past adventures, until he surpassed in favour all other men.

Communing with himself, the king determined to entrust the traveller with the ministry in chief; yet to do it with deliberation, that none might mock his plan as folly. " First," he thought, " I must test his wisdom and elevate his rank according to his merits. Many a heart is laden with grief when inexperience governs."* By every means he tested his capacities; the man was full of wisdom and his religion pure. The king perceived in him a man of upright character and clear reasoning, one who weighed his words and understood each man's work. Finding him thus better and wiser than all his nobles, he set him above the chief minister [in station], where he worked with such wisdom and understanding that no man's heart was sore at either his command or his prohibition, and his administration of the realm brought pain to no one. He tied the tongue of every caviller because his hands wrought no jot of evil. Through his illustrious mind the kingdom took on great splendour and the old vizier was afflicted with ever new jealousies, but he saw no flaw in the wise man's armour in which he could lodge an accusation. (The honourable man stands towards his rival like a metal tray

* Three lines of moralising in this strain omitted.

3

to the ant; the latter can find no flaw in the former.)

Now the king had two pages, handsome as the sun, who were always in his presence.* The sweet words of the sage took effect upon the two youths, and the kindliness of his ways made them his friends. He too had human liking for them, though not a liking for ill, as men of no understanding would have, only when his glance rested on their faces did he know real joy.† The old vizier watched the other's conduct for a time and then with evil intent informed the king,‡ [who considered] that just as he had not admitted the man to be his associate in the royal halls until his merits were proved, so now he ought not on the word of a rival to punish him for a fault unless it were proved. He concealed the matter in his heart for a time, remembering the word of the wise that the heart is the prison-house of secrets, which, once uttered, never return to their bonds. Privily he watched the man and observed the flaw in the sage's conduct; saw him suddenly fix his gaze upon one of the two youths who smiled covertly back. § The evil thought appeared proven to the king, and in his state of rage he would have vented his wrath upon him. Yet in the delicacy of his character and the perfection of his wisdom he spoke gently to the man. " O man

*Three lines of description omitted. †Three lines omitted.
‡ Sixteen lines omitted.   § Two lines omitted.

4

of goodly name," he said, "I considered you wise and entrusted the secrets of the kingdom to you. So lofty a rank is not your station. Yet the fault is of my own making; the blunder is not yours. When I raise to dignity a man of evil character he naturally considers it lawful to deal treacherously with me within my household."

Raising his head, the philosopher spoke thus to that monarch of wide experience: " Since my robe is unstained with any crime, I have no fear of the evil of any ill-wisher. The thought of what you say never entered my mind; I do not know who can have talked [so] of something I have never done."

" What I have said against you," replied the king, " your adversaries will say to your face. It was the old vizier who told me; do you now tell me and make clear what you know."

The other laughed and put his finger upon his lip in astonishment.

" Nothing that *he* says can be a cause for wonderment," he answered. " How can anything but evil of me be uttered by the tongue of an envious man who sees me occupy his own position? I set him down as my enemy from the moment when your Majesty deposed him in my favour. When the Sultan grants me precedence over him is it not certain that he will be an enemy at my heels? Not until the Resurrection will he let me be his friend, knowing that in my honour lies his humiliation. Let me tell you a story fitting this point, if you would incline your ear to your slave."

" I do not know where, but in some book, I have read that a man once saw the Devil in a dream. In form he was handsome as a pine-tree, his face worthy of a [celestial] houri; light shone from his face as though from the sun. The man approached him and asked: " Are you really this wonderful thing? No angel has beauty equal to yours. You have a face beautiful as the moon; why do they spread abroad in the world the report of your ugliness? They think your face inspires terror and in the public baths make drawings of you as a hideous thing. Why is the portrait of you in the king's palace a picture of something gruesome-faced, crooked-handed, hideous and corrupt? "

The unfortunate spirit heard the words and in anguish uttered a great cry.

' O blessed one,' he said, ' That is not a picture of me; the pencil is ever in an enemy's hand. I uprooted and cast them out of Paradise, and now, for revenge, they design me ugly.'

" In like fashion," continued the philosopher, " my name is good, but my enemy purposely will speak no good of me."*

" But," the king objected, " this is not what I heard from your rival, but what I saw myself

* Six lines omitted.

6

with my own eyes. It was not fitting that you should fix your glances on these two and on no one else of all my court."

He laughed, that eloquent man, and said:

" It is true; and the truth may not be concealed. Yet—may your rule continue and your fortune mighty—there is a subtle point in this, if you would hear it. Do you not see how the beggar, destitute of possessions keeps his eyes in envy upon the wealthy man? For me the possessions of youth are spent, in frivolity and pleasure my life has been wasted. I cannot refrain from looking at these two who have all the capital of beauty and splendour. Once I too had roses in my cheeks and my body was crystal-white in beauty. Now I have reached the stage for the weaving of my shroud, my hair being like the cotton and my body like the spindle. Once I too had tresses the colour of night, and my cloak in its fineness stretched tight across my chest. Two rows of pearls had a place in my mouth, firm as a wall with bricks of silver. Now, look, when I speak they fall one by one, like [bricks in] an old wall. Why should I not look upon these two in envy when I remember my life that is gone? Those happy days of mine are gone; this day too will come to a close without warning."

When the sage had strung together these pearls of wisdom, the king spoke:

" Better than that one could not say," and

7

looking at the notables of the land he continued:
" None can wish for truer word or sentiment."*

I have heard that Darius, of splendid lineage,
was separated from his train on the hunting-field.
A herdsman came towards him running and
Darius, he of blessed faith, saying to himself that
perhaps this was an enemy coming with hostile
intent, proposed to pierce him with an arrow at
some way off. On to his royal bow he fitted the
bow-string and would in a moment have brought
the fellow's life to nought, but he said:
" My lord of Irán and of Túr, may the evil eye
be far from your good fortune. I am the man that
rears the king's horses; I am in your service in
these pastures." The king's wit, gone for a moment, was restored to him. With a laugh he said:
" Your impulsiveness, my man, was dangerous.
Gabriel himself was your helper or else I should
have stretched the bow-string to my ear."
The keeper of the pastures laughed, and said:
"Good advice should not be withheld from a
benefactor. For a king not to know friend from
enemy means neither laudable government nor
efficient counsel. In a great man it is an essential
part of his life to know who each subordinate is.
Often have you seen me in your presence, and
asked me about your horses and your pastures.
Yet now when I come with affection before you,

* Graf's edition, pp. 42-54.

you do not know me again from an ill-wisher. O glorious king, I can pick out a horse from a hundred thousand; I apply my mind and thought to my herdsmanship. You too have your herd that follows you."

Darius heard the man's advice and gave him kindly word and treatment; then departed, calling shame upon himself and saying: " This counsel should be written on my heart."*

I have been told that one of the kings of Ghúr used by force to seize asses, which, unfed, bore their heavy loads for a day or two, then miserably perished.† I understand that that tyrannous monarch once set out into the hunting-field, and rode at full speed in chase of some game. Night overtook him at a moment when he was separated from his retinue, and not himself knowing the road or where he was, he found himself at last in a village. In it lived an old man who had for long known the various ranks of men. He spoke to his son and said:

" This morning do not take your donkey into the city. This malevolent and unblest fellow, for whom I see a coffin in place of his throne, has his loins girt in the service of the devil, and the cry against his oppression has reached to heaven. No man has ever seen, nor will ever see peace or joy in this land until this black-omened and vile

* Graf's edition, pp. 61-63.
† Two lines omitted.

9

scoundrel descends to hell with curses at his back."

" But," replied the youth, " the way to the city is long. I cannot travel it afoot, blessed one. Think of some plan and give me counsel; for your reasoning is better than mine."

" If you will listen to my counsel," said the father, " you will take a big stone and strike the pack-ass several blows with it, wounding the animal in the head, the leg and the side. Then perhaps the donkey will not suffer the fate of being worked by that vile fellow of hideous faith."*

The son heard his father's speech, and did not withdraw from the line of his command. Down on to the unfortunate donkey he brought the stone until its fore-leg was helpless and its hind leg lamed.

" Now," said the father, " carry out what you wish and go your way."

The son fell in at the tail of a caravan and walked along reviling [the king] with all his might. His father, for his part, raised his hands aloft to heaven and cried:

" O Lord, by the prayer-rug of the saints, grant me security from fate until destruction carries off this accursed oppressor. If I see not his downfall, my eye—blind with night—will not sleep in the grave."

* Two lines omitted.

The king heard it all, and, with his saddle for a pillow, he lay down to sleep. But the whole night long in wakefulness he counted the stars: sleep would not relieve him of angry thought. Only when he heard the voice of the bird of dawn did he forget the night's distraction. All night his troopers had galloped about, and in the morning recognised his horse's tracks. From horseback they saw him afoot on the plain and ran towards him to place their heads on the ground in obeisance. The land, with wave upon wave of troops, resembled the sea, while the chieftains called for food and having eaten, sat in council.

One amongst the oldest of the king's friends, his chamberlain at night his courtier by day, asked him what hospitality his subjects had shown him that night. " For none of us," he continued, " rested eye or ear all night."

The monarch could not tell the story of his wretched fate, but quietly he inclined his head towards the other and privily, in low tones, he said: "No one brought me even the leg of a fowl, but the leg of a donkey grew to great size."

When cheerfulness returned to his soul the king remembered the peasant of the night before. At his orders they sought the man out, bound him fast and flung him down in humiliation at the throne's foot. The black-hearted prince drew his sword so that the wretch before him, seeing no way of escape, and counting that moment the last in his life, spoke what lay in his heart. (Do you not see how much more fluently the reed-pen writes when the knife is at its head?) He raised his head in his desperation, and said:

" It is useless to lie at home on the night when the grave is ready for us. Not I alone, O king, have said that you are a man of accurst fortune and evil fate. It is not only I who have sounded the trumpet against your wrong-doing, but a whole people. If you slay me, I am but one of a multitude. Through the cruelty that surrounds you the whole world is filled with report of your oppressions. Your hope lies in turning from your wrong-doing, and not in slaying one who is un-offending and helpless. Remember that you have a few short days to live; in even less time than that you will have expended the sweets of life. Of what benefit to you is it, then, to receive the plaudits of the crowd while old women behind their spinning-wheels utter curses on you? "

Thus he spoke with the sword over his head, surrendering his soul to dark fate. The stupor of the king's self-deception gave way to under-standing as into his ear the archangel Gabriel spoke:

" Stay your hand from punishing this ancient man. Remember he will be only one slain out of myriads."

The king's head remained sunk in thought for a while within his collar, and then he stretched out his hand in pardon. Himself he loosed the bonds and took them off the man, kissed his head and took him to his heart; then gave him great and lofty rank, so that fine fruit came from the branch of his hope.*

A certain athlete, so lacking in good fortune that for his sustenance he had enough neither for supper nor for breakfast, was forced by his belly to carry mud on his back, for he could earn no food with his fists. Through the wretchedness of his circumstances his heart was for ever defiled by envy and his body miserable. Sometimes his battle with a malevolent world made him clench his fist, sometimes his face was sour at his unhappy lot; at other times the sight of others' sweet pleasure made him swallow the waters of bitterness; again, overwhelmed with toil, he wept. None ever had a more bitter existence.

" Some," he said, " have honey to eat, and chicken and lamb, but the surface of my bread never sees a savoury. If you seek for equity surely it is not right that I should go naked while the very cat has a fur! If only my foot, in this miry work, would sink down to some treasure to delight my heart! I swear if I could turn fate to my desires I would shake off the dust of toil from myself."

I heard that one day while he was digging the

* Pp. 102-112.

soil, he found a dried jaw-bone, of which the ligaments had been destroyed in the ground, and the teeth had all fallen out. The tongueless mouth uttered good counsel and a secret, telling him to be content with lack of wealth.

" Is not my condition," it asked, " that of any mouth in the dust, whether it ate sugar or heart's blood? Do not grieve at the turn of fortune's wheel, for it will turn for long enough without our presence."

From the moment when this thought came to him, the youth packed his sorrows to one side and said:

" O foolish heart, unreasoning and senseless, have patience with your load of care and do not slay yourself. Whether a man is a slave bearing a load on his head or whether he holds his head high as zenith, when fortune changes each loses his head in death. Neither grief nor joy lasts, but the reward of one's labour and one's good name continues."*

* Pp. 117-120.

ON GENEROSITY

I HAVE heard that during one week no voyager visited the guest chamber of Abraham, friend of Allah. In blessedness of spirit he would not break his fast unless some hapless traveller came to him from the road; and so he went forth to look about him on every side. In the recesses of a valley he espied a man alone, like a willow in a waterless spot, his head and beard white with the snow of eld. Heartily he gave him welcome and invited him, as a nobleman would, to the feast, saying:

" O pupil of my eyes, be generous enough to eat my bread and salt."

The other consented, leaping up and hastening his pace, for he knew the habit of the saint, upon whom be peace! The wardens of Abraham's guest-chamber seated the humble old man with honour. At Abraham's command they spread a table and all seated themselves about it, but when they began " In Allah's name," no sound from the old man came to the saint's hearing. He addressed him thus:

" O ancient of days, I see no such piety and

15

burning zeal in you as befits the aged. Is it not a duty that when you eat your daily bread, you should mention the name of him that provides it?"

The man replied: "I do not believe it. I never follow a practice I have not heard of from my Zoroastrian teacher."

The prophet of goodly fate then understood that the old man, so fallen on evil days, was a fire-worshipper, and seeing him of foreign faith, drove him away with contumely, saying that it was a sin for the impure to remain with the clean. From the Almighty there came the archangel Gabriel in awfulness to rebuke him:

"O Friend, for a hundred years I gave him daily bread and life; you were wearied of him in a moment. Even though he prostrates himself in worship of fire, why should you withhold the hand of generosity?"*

Tie no knot in the fastening of generosity, saying: "This is fraud and trickery; that is guile and deceit."

The man of perspicacity does ill to sell his learning and culture for bread. Where does either reason or law sanction wise men's bartering religion for the worldly things? Yet receive them, for the wise man buys eagerly from them that sell cheap.

* Pp. 142 ff.

A man of eloquent tongue once came to a saint and said:

" I am sunk deep in the mire, being indebted to some vile fellow in the sum of ten dirhams. An obol from him weighs like ten maunds on my heart, so that my nights are spent in misery through him, and every day he is at my heels like a shadow. His wild words have opened a wound in my heart wide as a door; it were as though God had never given him from his birth anything but these ten dirhams. He is ignorant of the first letter in the book of religion, and he has read nothing [in the grammar of life] but the section on indeclinables. The sun has scarcely risen above the hill-tops, but that rogue is hammering at the knocker on my door. Therefore I have been considering whether some generous friend would not help me with silver against the stony-hearted fellow."

The ancient, blessed of soul, heard his words and put two golden coins within his sleeve. They fell into the palm of him that spun the tale, and he left the house with a face as bright as the coins. Someone asked the saint if he did not know who the fellow was, and said that if he died there would be no cause for grief.

" He is a beggar who could saddle a male lion and, playing chess, could give to the famous Abu Zaid a knight and the queen."

The pious man was roused.

"Be silent," he said. "Since you have no skill with your tongue, give ear. Even if what I think were true, I respected his honour before men, and if he has been bold and impudent, do not accuse him of fraud. For I have (in this) guarded my own honour against this cunning speaker of baseless words."*

It was told me that a certain old man on the road to [holy] Hejaz said two prayers for every step he took and walked so zealously in the path of God that he did not stop even to pluck the thorns from his foot. But there came a time when, by the instigation of a seducer, his conduct found favour in his own eyes. Through the Devil's cunning he fell into the pit of saying that no better road than his own was possible; and, if he had not found God's mercy, false pride would have turned his head from the true path. A voice from Heaven came to him out of the void and said:

"O fortunate man of blessed spirit, think not that if you have obeyed God's will you have found a footing at his court. To compose your heart by well-doing were better than a thousand prayers in every stage [of your road]." †

The wife of a Sultan's officer once bid him rise and knock at livelihood's door. "Go," said she,

* Pp. 143-146.　　　† Pp. 151-152.

18

" let them give you a portion from their table, on which your children's looks are fixed."

He said: "The king's kitchen will be cold to-day, for in the night he proposed to celebrate a fast."

The woman in despair cast down her head and to herself she said, her heart sore with fasting: "What does the king mean by this fasting, when the breaking of his fast means a feast for our children?"

An eater whose hand brings benefits is better than a man who is always fasting but worships the things of this world. Let him freely enjoy his fast who gives the poor enough bread for a breakfast. Apart from that, what need is there to put yourself out, when you yourself eat up what you have withheld from yourself? The thoughts of the fool in private may lead him to confuse heresy with faith. *

There was a man once, possessed of generosity, but without power to satisfy it, his means not being equal to his nobility of character. (May no mean creature ever be lord of creation, and may never a generous man be afflicted with poverty! He whose aim is high does not often find his quarry in the net, just as the spate pouring down never finds a lodgment on the mountain side.)

Now the subject of our story gave largesse beyond his substance, and of necessity therefore became straitened in means. To him, nevertheless,

* Pp. 152 f.

a friend in embarrassed circumstances wrote a short letter saying: " O you of goodly fate, man of blessed soul, come to my rescue with a few dirhams. For some time now I have been lodged in prison."

In the generous man's eyes the amount was as nothing, but in his hand there was not a stiver. He sent to the prisoner's creditors and said: "Men of goodly fame, noblemen; withhold your hands from his skirts for awhile. If he flees, I will be bail for him." From them he proceeded to the prison, where he bade the debtor rise and run as long as his feet held. Like a sparrow seeing the door of his cage open, his delay did not last a moment. Like the morning wind he travelled from that land so fast that the wind could not overtake him with his own dust.

The creditors at once seized the benefactor, telling him to produce either the money or the man, and, being incapable of either, he took the road to the prison; for once a bird has left its nest it cannot be retaken. I hear that he remained in captivity for a long period, writing no complaint and uttering no lament, although during that time he was never at peace and he could not sleep at night. One day a pious friend passed that way and said: " I did not think you were a man to consume another's property. What has happened to make them put you into prison? "

He replied: " My friend of blessed soul, I have

consumed no one's property by guile. I saw a
helpless fellow tormented by fetters, and saw no
way for his release except my own imprisonment.
My mind did not approve my being happy whilst
another was in the trap."

He died in the end, and left a good name behind.
Happy the life that leaves a deathless name! A
body that has perished, but has a heart that is
alive beneath the ground, is better than a living
worldling with his heart dead. The living heart
never perishes. What fear is there that the body
with its heart alive will ever die?*

A dervish lamented on the misery of his fate
to a rich man of angry visage, who, black-hearted
wight, gave him neither dinar nor obol and, as
an extra slight, shouted at him in a rage. The
beggar's heart filled with woe at the wrong;
raising his head in grief, he said:

" I wonder why the wealthy man is so sour of
face. Has he no fear of the bitterness of beggary?"

The other, in lack of vision, then gave his men
orders to drive the wretch away with humiliation
and vile insults.

It was told me that through his ingratitude to
the Provider, the rich man's fortunes were re-
versed. His greatness was headed for destruction,
and Mercury dipped his pen in blackness. Poverty
stripped the man as naked as garlic, leaving him

* Pp. 153-155.

neither pack nor animal to bear it. Fate settled the dust of poverty on his head, so that he came to resemble a gambler with pocket and hand both empty. From head to foot his circumstances changed.

Some time now passed after the occurrence. The man's slave had fallen into the hands of a generous patron; a man expansive in heart and power, of noble soul, who had rejoiced as much at seeing this unhappy wretch as a beggar at the sight of wealth. One night there came to this patron's door a beggar, whose steps dragged through what he had suffered of great hardships. The far-sighted master of the house bade his slave make the destitute fellow happy. When the servant approached with a portion from the table, a cry broke from him involuntarily. With a broken heart he returned to his master, with tears proclaiming the preface of his secret. The nobleman blessed of fortune asked whose hurt it was had brought the tears to his cheek. He replied:

" My heart is sorely grieved at the condition of this unfortunate old man. In time past I was his slave, and he was owner of possessions, lands and money; but his hand no longer achieves honour and ease; he stretches it out to beg from door to door."

The master laughed and said:

" No wrong has been done here, my son; no

one may revile the turn of fortune's wheel. Is he not that angry-visaged merchant who held his head aloft arrogantly into the skies? I am the man he drove from his door with violence that day; the revolution of the world has put him in my place. Heaven has looked favourably on me once more, and swept the dust of hardship from my face. When God in his wisdom closes one door, in his generosity and mercy he opens another. Many a penniless man, without any means, has been satisfied, and many a rich man's career has been turned upside down."*

On the road once a youth came towards me with a sheep following him at a gallop. I said to him:

" Is it a rope or a chain that makes the sheep follow at your heels? "

Swiftly he loosened the collar from it and removed the chain and it began to run to right and left. But again it returned at his heels, for it had eaten barley and green corn from his hand. When it came back to its place after gambolling and playing, he looked at me and said: " O goodly counsellor, it is not the rope that carries it along with me, kindness rather is the bond about its neck. Because of the bounty which the raging elephant has received it will not attack its keeper. Therefore, honest man, deal kindly with the wicked, for a dog will keep guard if it has eaten

* Pp. 157-160.

23

your bread; the panther's teeth are blunted for the man whose cheese its tongue has licked, be it only for two days." *

I once heard there was a man of noble origin, learned and zealous, in the confines of Turkey. With seven travellers experienced in desert paths I went to visit him. He kissed the eyes and head of every one of us, likewise our hands; with great ceremony and honour he bade us be seated and himself sat down. I saw he had gold and lands, servants and gear, but he was as bare of generosity as a tree without fruit. He was a man ready with his polished manners and politenesses, but the grate beneath his saucepan was very cold. Never a night did he rest or sleep for saying his prayers, nor we for hunger. In the morning he girt up his loins and opened our door and again began his politeness and kissings. Now there was a man of sweet and witty temper, a fellow-traveller, who was lodged with us.

" Change your spelling of ' kisses,' " said he, "for to a beggar ' dishes ' sounds better than ' kisses.' Don't be for ever putting your hands on my shoes in obeisance. Give me food and you may strike me on the head with my shoe."†

I have heard that Hatim in his day had amongst his horses one that was swift-footed as smoke :

* Pp. 162 f.   † Pp. 165 f.

24

a bay, with the speed of the morning wind and thundering hoofs, out-stripping the lightning. As in his gallop he dripped sweat on mountain and plain you might have said an April cloud had passed over. Men told the king of Rúm something of Hatim's fame which was spread abroad in every land, saying no man was his peer for generosity nor was there the equal of his horse in the race or the battle, as it sailed over the plain like a ship over the waters, so that not even the raven could fly at its pace.

To his wise minister the king then spoke as follows:

" To make a claim without fulfilling it would be a disgrace. I will pray Hatim for that Arab horse. If he is generous and grants it, I shall know that great honour is due to him; but if he refuses it, all [his fame is] nothing but the sound of an empty drum."

Accordingly, with an escort of ten men he sent a skilled and learned messenger to Tayy. The ground [they traversed] was dead and the clouds wept over it, but the morning wind again brought life to it. They alighted then at Hatim's encampment, as glad as the thirsty man at sight of a flowing stream. He spread a table and slaughtered a horse for food; into their laps he poured sugar, and gold into their hands. They slept the night there. In the morning the bearer of the message spoke what he had to say; and, as he spoke, Hatim became distracted as a man in drink, and bit his hands in anguish.

"O man of happy lot, sage of good fame," he exclaimed. "Why did you not give me your message before this? Last night to make meat for you I slew that wind-paced steed, swift as Duldul,* because I knew that through the fearsome rain and flood it was not possible to go to the horses' pasture-ground. No other course or plan was open to me; that horse alone stood at my palace door, and I saw it would not be hospitality befitting my character if my guest should go to sleep with his heart aggrieved through hunger. I require my fame to be spread abroad in the land; compared with that you may call the famous steed a thing of no importance."

Upon the men he lavished money and honours and horses; for kindly qualities were natural to him and not love of gain. News of the generous man of Tayy spread then in Rúm—a thousand blessings were showered upon him.

Yet be not content with this trifle on Hatim's account; listen to the story of an even more noble deed. I know not who told me this tale. It is of a ruler who lived in Yemen and who carried off the ball of success amongst men of fame, for in his lavish giving he had no peer. It may be said of him he was the cloud of liberality, since his hand scattered money like rain. No one ever

* The mule of the Caliph 'Alí.

mentioned the name of Hatim to him, for fear
of incurring his rage.

"How many stories," he would ask, "will
you tell me of that man who is of no more substance than air, and who has neither kingship,
nor authority, nor treasure?"

I have been told he prepared a royal feast, and
while the music was being played in the crowded
assembly one guest opened the subject of Hatim,
whom another began to praise. Envy drew on
the prince to fury and he appointed a man to slay
Hatim; for, he reasoned, as long as Hatim remained in the world with him, his own name
would never stand for beneficence.

The assassin made the journey to the Baní Tayy
with intent to kill the benefactor, and on the road
he met a youth who came towards him with an
air of regard and friendliness. A man he was of
handsome face, cultured and pleasant-tongued,
and he bore off the traveller to be his guest that
night. Nobly he entertained him, meantime
expressing his solicitude and uttering excuses, so
that with his kindliness he captured the heart of
his malevolent guest. Moreover in the morning he
kissed his hand and foot and prayed he would
remain with him for several days. The other said:

"I cannot for long continue here, for I have
a difficult task before me."

He replied:

"If you will propound it to me, I will use every

27

effort of my soul to help you as much as if we were bosom friends."

"Most generous man," he said, "give ear, for I know that a generous man keeps secrets veiled. Do you perchance know Hatim in this land, a man of blessed thought and bountiful character? The king of Yemen demands his head, for I know not what quarrel that has arisen between them. If you will direct me to his encampment, that will be all I desire from your favour."

The young man laughed and said: "I am Hatim. Here is my head. Sever it with your sword from my body. It must never be that when the morning dawns any harm should come to you, or that you should be put into desperate straits."

When Hatim thus nobly laid his head down, a cry came from the other's soul. Into the dust he fell, rejoicing; kissed now the ground and now Hatim's hands and feet. His sword he flung aside and laid down his quiver; like one who surrendered all hope he laid his hands upon his breast and said:

"Were I to fling even a rose at you with intent to harm, I should be a woman, not a man, in men's sight."

Hatim kissed both his eyes and pressed him to his heart, and the man departed thence on the way back to Yemen.

The king knew from between his agent's eyebrows that he had not carried out his task. "Come,

tell me what news you bring," he said. " Why is
not the head tied to your saddle-bow? Was it his
fame overwhelmed you, that you did not apply
your strength to give him battle? "

The cunning youth, prostrate on the ground,
uttered the king's praises and flattered him, then
said:

" I found Hatim, that seeker after fame, a man
of parts, of splendid appearance and handsome
face. I saw he was generous and the possessor of
wisdom, and in manly qualities even richer than
is told of him. The load of his bounty bended me
double and he defeated me with the sword of
beneficence and favour." He then recounted what
he had seen of Hatim's benefactions until the
king uttered praises on the family of Tayy. He
sealed the messenger's services with money, for
liberality is the seal inscribed with Hatim's name.*

There was once a man who could not bear to
spend money. He had gold but was incapable of
enjoying it. He did not feast to find enjoyment,
nor did he give anything away, thinking: " To-
morrow it will be of use." Night and day he was
bound by the fetters of gold and silver, gold and
silver bonds held that unhappy man. His son one
day out of concealment discovered the hiding-
place in the ground in which the man had secreted
his gold. He lifted it out of the ground and scat-

* Pp. 167-172.

tered it to the winds—I have been told he put a stone in its place. The gold did not last with the young man, it came into one hand and he expended it with the other. His losses increased, matters went ill with him, until he pledged even his hat and loin-cloth in the market-place.

Meantime the father clutched himself by the throat while the son clawed at the harp and made music in the throat of the reed-pipe. Through weeping and wailing the father did not sleep all night, and in the morning the son came laughing and said:

"Gold was meant for spending, father; if it were meant to lay by, a stone were as good as gold. Gold is got from flinty ore for us to enjoy it with our companions and friends. Gold in the hands of a worldly man is still in the ore. If in your lifetime you quarrel with your family, do not complain if they pray for your death. Only when you have fallen from a roof fifty cubits high will your family enjoy themselves to the full at your expense. A miser rich in dinars and silver is merely a talisman set over his treasure. His gold only lasts for so many years because so awful a talisman trembles over it. But suddenly the talisman is broken by the stone of fate, and joyfully men divide the treasure. After you have brought and gathered it like an ant, devour it; before the worm of the grave devours you." *

* Pp. 182 f.

A youth once gave a copper to a beggar, an old man who craved it from him. Fate seized the youth for some crime, and the Sultan sent him to the place of execution, where there was the galloping of Turks and the general turmoil of the crowd looking on at the spectacle from doorway, street, and roof. The old beggar saw the youth in anguish, a prisoner in the hands of others. His heart was grieved for that miserable youth, whose heart he once had wrung. [Suddenly] he raised a cry: " The Sultan is dead; the world remains; but he leaves fair fame after him." He twisted his hands together in grief [as he spoke]. The Turks with drawn swords heard his lament, and with a shout, raining blows on heads and faces and backs, they rushed on foot back to the palace, where, on his throne, they saw the king.

The youth disappeared meanwhile, and the old man was seized and brought to the Sultan's throne. In terrible and awe-inspiring rage he questioned him:

" What reason had you for desiring my death, though my dealings are generous and upright? Why should you wish anyone ill? "

The courageous old man loosened his tongue and said:

" O sovereign, the world is but a ring in the ear of thy authority! You did not really die through the lying report of your death, and thereby an unhappy wretch saved his life."

The king was so amazed at his words that he made him a gift and said nothing.

Meantime the unhappy youth ran till he fell, rose again and continued his flight hither and thither. Someone asked him how he had escaped from the cross-roads of the gallows. He whispered in the other's ear: " Wise man, by means of my generous heart and a copper I was rescued from my fetters."*

I have heard that once a maiden, beautiful as a fairy, broke into a dance at a minstrel's playing. And while she kindled every heart about her, a candle's flame set the hem of her robe ablaze. She ran about in wild distraction, when one of her lovers spoke and said:

" What is your fear? The fire burns only the edge of your robe, but my whole being is ablaze."

If you are a lover, think not only of yourself, for it were heresy to worship both the loved one and yourself.†

A man once loved a maiden in Samarcand, so witty, you would have said the words from her mouth were lumps of sugar. She had beauty enough to lend to the sun, and her wit laid piety's foundations in ruins. Heavens above! so great was her loveliness you would have said it was a special sign of God's bounty. Wherever she went

* Pp. 183-185.   † Pp. 198 f.

glances followed her; her lovers would all have given their lives for her.

Now the man kept secret watch upon the maiden. She observed it one day and said in anger:

" How long, you impudent fellow, will you be galloping at my heels? If you do not know it, I am not a bird in your net; and if I see you again I will cut off your head with a sword without any hesitation."

A friend heard and said to him: " Go your own way now and find some object more easily attained. I do not think you can achieve this desire of your heart. Beware not to lose your soul for your heart's sake."

The distraught lover, who had lost his heart, at her reviling cried aloud in grief: " Let the wound made by destruction's sword tumble me, a corpse, in the blood and mire. Perhaps both enemy and friend will then know that it was by her hands and sword I was slain. Yet I can see no hope of escape from the dust of the street in which she lives.* If I were to expire to-day in the street of my beloved's dwelling, yet on the day of Resurrection I should pitch my tent by my loved one's side." †

A newly wedded wife complains to an old man of her spouse's unamiable qualities. " Do not say you approve of my spending the rest of my life

* Three lines omitted.   † Pp. 202 f.

in bitterness with the youth," she said. "Amongst
the other people who live in the same house with
us I see no one so unhappy as myself; husband
and wife love one another so much you would
say they were two souls in one body. But during
all this time I have never once seen my husband
smile into my face."

The aged man listened. He was a man of happy
disposition, wise and old in years. His reply was
sweet and pleasant.

"If he is handsome, bear with the burden of
him. It would be a pity to turn away from a man
whose equal you may not find again. Why turn
away from one whose departure from you would
mean the destruction of your life? Acquiesce
like a slave in the will of God, for you will discover no master like Him."*

There was a doctor of Merv, handsome as a
peri, whose figure was a cypress in the garden
of love. But he was unconscious of the pain he
brought to many hearts, nor had he any thought
for those who languished because of his eyes. A
patient from a distance once said: "I am so
enamoured of my physician, that I have no desire
to find health again and be without occasion to
call my doctor in." †

A man once made an iron fist with which he

* Pp. 207 f.   † Pp. 208 f.

intended to try his strength against lions. But once when he was caught by a lion in its clutches he no longer saw any use for his fist. A friend called out to him: " Why are you asleep like a woman? Why not trounce the lion with that fist of yours?" I have been told that the miserable wretch spoke from underneath [the beast, and said]: " It is useless to fight lions with this kind of fist." When love conquers a wise man, the resemblance is with this iron fist and the lion. In the grip of lion-like men you are a woman; of what use to you is an iron fist? If love comes, speak no more of reason, for the ball is a prisoner in the crook of the polo-stick.*

It happened in a land of the West that I and an old man from Faryab arrived at a stream. I had a dirham and they took me into a boat, leaving the old man. The Ethiop boatmen then drove the vessel along as fast as smoke, for the captain was a man without fear of God. Grief for my friend brought tears to my eyes, but he laughed and said: " Have no care for me, wise friend. He that bore the ship across will transport me also." He spread his prayer-carpet on the surface of the water and I asked myself whether I fancied or dreamt it. Greatly troubled, my eyes did not close in sleep that night. In the morning my friend looked at me and said: " You were astonished,

* Pp. 209 f.

my friend of happy counsel; the boat brought you across and God brought me. Why do people of pretensions not believe that saints may traverse water and fire? When a child knows nothing of fire its mother watches lovingly over it. So those who are sunk in pious ecstasy are the centre of God's care day and night."*

A village chieftain on a journey with his son passed by the centre of a royal army. The boy beheld the officers and the swords and battle-axes, saw the coats of satin and the waist-belts of gold, the gallant bowmen and the hunters, the slave quiver-bearers and the archers. One there was who wore a silken cloak, another had a royal helmet on his head. The boy looked on all the pomp and circumstance and then saw his father greatly humbled, with his dignity so reduced and his self-respect so lost that he fled to a cave. The boy said to him:

"After all, you are chief of the village. In dignity you are greater than these chieftains. What made you cast off your hopes from life so that you trembled like a willow in the wind of terror?"

"True," he replied, "I am a leader and have authority, but my dignity extends only as far as my village. Even great men are afflicted with terror when they visit the court of the king. You,

* Pp. 215 f.

36

my innocent one, are so much part of your village
that you fancy yourself possessing authority.*
Have you not seen in garden and meadow a little
worm that glows in the night like a lamp? Someone said to it once: ' O little worm that illumines
the night, why do you not appear in the daytime? '
Note what the earth-born worm of fire said, and
what an illuminating reply it gave: ' I am in the
open night and day, but in the sunlight I cannot
be seen.' "†

A moth was once addressed thus: " Poor
wretch, go and find a lover more fitted to yourself. Travel on a path which you may consider a
hopeful way. How are you suited to love a candle
flame? You are neither a salamander to hover
round a fire, nor have you the valour which is
necessary for combat. The blind bat hides itself
from the sun, for it would be folly to attack an
armoured champion; and to take for your friend
one whom you know to be your enemy would
not be an act of reason. Thus also no one will say
you do well to put your life into relationship with
hers. The beggar who asked the king for his
daughter received only blows and nourished false
hopes. How can she bring you into the tale of her
lovers when the eyes of kings and sultans turn
towards her? Cease to think that in company of
that kind she will have any compliments to spare

* Line omitted.   † Pp. 216 f.

for a penniless wight like you. And even if she is gentle towards all the world she will be harsh to you, miserable wretch."

Hear what the moth, aflame, replied:

" You that marvel, tell me what fear there is that I shall burn. Like Abraham, I have so great a fire in my heart you would think this flame of hers were a rose by its side. It is not my heart that attracts the hem of her robe [the flame] to me, but my love of her which drags my soul by force to her.* How long will you tell me to find for myself a companion suitable and sympathetic to me? In my unhappy condition it is as if you told a boy stung by a scorpion not to cry. You stand astonished; but never give advice when you know it cannot be put into effect. To the wretched driver who has lost the reins, they never say: ' Drive slowly, boy! ' How delightful is the witticism in Sindbad: ' Love is fire, my son, and advice is wind.' " †

---

* Six lines omitted.   † Pp. 224-227.

ON HUMILITY

A DROP of rain fell from a cloud, and was humbled when it saw the vastness of the ocean. " What can I be," it thought, " when the sea is here? If it has a place here then surely I have none." While it regarded itself thus with the eye of contempt, an oyster took it to her heart and nourished it with care. Heaven so favoured its lot that it became a famous royal pearl.*

I have heard that once on the morning of a festival, Báyazíd [the warrior] had just come forth from the warm baths, when from a house someone without warning poured down a basinful of ashes on his head. With his turban and hair polluted, and rubbing his face with his hands, he said thankfully: " Oh, for my lusts I deserve the fire; shall I frown at a handful of ash? " †

A man learned in the law, but wearing ancient garments in his poverty, seated himself amongst the company in the cadi's house. The cadi looked

* Pp. 230 f.   † Pp. 232 f.

at him very sharply, and the major domo seized him by the sleeve and bade him rise, asking him if he knew not that he had placed himself in a seat too high for his station. " Either take a humbler place, or leave, or stand. Not everyone is worthy of the seat of honour; honour goes by excellence and rank by worth."* When the impoverished sage understood that his fate had led him into a dispute [on a point of etiquette], a sigh like fire came from him and he seated himself in a place even humbler than was his right.

It happened that the lawyers present had come prepared to wrangle. " Why?"'s and " we do not agree "s began to be hurled about, and the door of conflict was opened wide, while each man pompously uttered his " Nay " or " Yea." You would have thought that a barn-yard full of clever cocks had fallen to quarrelling with beaks and spurs. Here was one like a drunken man, intoxicated with rage; there another beating both hands on the ground [as he sat]. They came at last upon a knotty point, tangle on tangle, and in the unravelling of it could make no headway. The old man, seated in the humblest rank, with a roar like a ravening lion, entered the fray, and said:

" My lords of the Prophet's law; in discussing Koranic transmission, revelation, ordinances and

* Three lines omitted.

legal principles, firm proof, sound and logical arguments are necessary, rather than the display of the angry veins in one's neck. I too have a mallet and a ball in this game."

They said:

" If you know anything to the point, declare it."

In dignified fashion he knelt, loosened his tongue so that the others fastened their mouths. With the pen of eloquence he graved his explanation on their hearts as a picture is drawn on a seal ring. By the lane of appearance he came to reality and drew his pen through the claim in dispute. From every side there came cries of " bravo " to him, and a thousand congratulations on his reasoning and skill. He drove the bay horse of eloquence so far that the cadi, remaining behind like an ass in the mire, dropped his cloak and turban and sent them as a gift to the old man in admiration, and said:

" Alas, I did not recognise your worth, and gave no thanks when you came. It grieves me now to see you with all your merit seated in so humble a place."

The major domo approached him now in friendly guise to place the cadi's turban on his head, but with hand and tongue he prevented him. " Keep your distance," he said. " Do not place upon my head the proud man's fetters, which to-morrow will weigh my head down with fifty yards of stuff against the wretches in worn-out clothes. When they call me ' my lord ' and put me in the high place of honour, men will be contemptible in my eyes. But is there any difference in crystal water if the jug that contains it be of gold or earthenware? What a man needs is wisdom and a brain inside his head; I am in no need, like you, of a fine turban. Because a man has a big head he does not therefore become something great. A gourd has a big head, but it is without pith."*

In this fashion the man of cunning speech with the water of his words washed the rancour from his heart. The words of an outraged man are harsh. When your enemy falls, bestir yourself. When your foeman's brain is within your reach, dash it out, for opportunity washes the dust [of wrath] from the heart.

The cadi was so taken aback by the man's taunts that he piously exclaimed: " This is indeed a calamitous day! " With astonishment he bit his hands, and his two eyes remained fixed upon the aged beggar like the two guardian stars of the Pole. But he turned his attention thence in another direction, and going outside [disappeared] and none could find trace of him again. A cry arose from the company: " Whence came this impudent fellow? " An officer went in search of him and looked about on every side asking

* Nine lines in the same spirit omitted.

who had seen a man of such and such a description and appearance. Someone said to him:

" The only man we know in this city with that kind of sweet inspiration is Sa'dí and no one else. A hundred thousand blessings on him for having spoken thus. See with what sweetness he told the bitter truth! "*

A dog bit the foot of a Bedouin with such fury that poison dripped from its teeth and the pain at night was so great that sleep could not comfort him. Now in his household he had a little daughter who upbraided him and was very angry. "Did you too not have teeth? " she asked. The unhappy man ceased his wailing and said, laughing: " My darling little mother, even though I had the power and a spear too, yet it would revolt me to use my own jaws and teeth. It would be impossible for me to apply my teeth to a dog's leg even if a sword were held at my head." The nature of dogs is evil, but man cannot [in defence] act like a dog.†

I remember that Nile, the water-carrier, one year brought no gift of water to Egypt. A company of people travelled to the mountains praying with loud supplication for rain. But from their weeping no stream came flowing save with the tears from the women's eyes. News of their plight was brought to Zú 'l Nún, saying: ' The people

* Pp. 239-244. † P. 253.

suffer much woe and hardship; pray therefore for these unfortunate ones, for the words of one acceptable to God are not turned aside.' I heard then that Zú 'l Nún fled to Midian. No long time passed before rain poured down. After twenty years news came to Midian that the black-hearted cloud had shed tears over Egypt, whereupon the saint resolved quickly to return, for the pools had filled with the spring floods. In secret an understanding man asked him. 'What wisdom was there in thy going thus?' He replied: 'I heard that upon fowl, ant and beast of prey, would come sore straits through the deeds of evil men. In this clime I had observed much, but saw none more full of sin than I was: therefore I went, lest through mine evil the door of good might be closed against the multitude.'*

* Pp. 283 f.

ON RESIGNATION

I H A D a friend at Isfahan who was warlike, bold and cunning. His hand and dagger were ever stained with blood, and the hearts of his enemies were on fire through him. There was not a day when I did not see him tying on his quiver, and fire leaping from his steel arrows. He was brave and strong, with the violence of a bull, so that lions fell into panic through terror of him. He sent his shafts with such good aim that he shot through both the Twins with one arrow. I never saw thorns pierce as his arrows pierced through thick shields. He never struck an opponent through the crown that he did not shatter both his helmet and head. In the fray he resembled a sparrow on a day of locusts, and in the killing a man was to him of as much account as a locust.* None ever saw his like in the world either for manly qualities or for magnanimity, and not for a moment did he ever leave my side, for he had a taste for persons of a loyal nature.

Travel suddenly snatched me away from that

* Four lines omitted.

land, for I found no livelihood there; and fate transported me from Iraq to Syria, in which pure soil I found a pleasant footing. To abbreviate my story; I made residence there for some time, suffering what came of toil and ease, of hope and fear.

Then once more, my cup over full of Syria, longing for home drew me back. Chance led my way home through Iraq, where one night, as I sat with my head sunk in thought, memory of that gallant friend [of Isfahan] passed through my mind. The salt [of desire] opened my old wound afresh, for I had eaten salt from the man's hand. I set out therefore for Isfahan and in love began to look about and seek for him. I found that with the passage of time the youth had grown old; his arrow form was bowed; his deep red complexion turned pale, the snowy hair on his head made him like the White Mountain with water from the snow of old age trickling down his face. Heaven had laid a heavy hand upon him and wrested aside the force of his strength. The world had driven pride out of his head and it was bowed low in weakness.

I said to him:

" O chieftain, taker of lions, what has made you as withered as an old fox? "

With a laugh, he replied:

" From the time of the war with the Tartars I have put the desire for war out of my head. I saw

46

the ground then as full of spears as a reed-bed of
reeds, and the [red] standards amongst them
[were] like fire. I raised the dust of battle like
smoke, but when power is lacking, of what use is
boldness? I am the man who could pick a ring
out of the hand when I attacked with the lance,
but since my star would not aid me, they sur-
rounded me in a ring. I took advantage of a way
of flight, for only a fool will battle hard with fate.
What help could my headpiece and cuirass give
me, when my bright star would not assist? If the
key to victory is not in one's hand, no arm can
break down the door to conquest. There was
with the enemy an army of leopard-breakers, men
of elephant strength, their heads and the horses'
hoofs being clad with iron. When we saw the
dust of that force we donned our mail and our
armoured helmets. Like a cloud we urged our
Arab steeds forward and poured down our
arrows like rain. Both armies rushed forward
from ambush with a shock as though the skies
had been dashed down upon the earth, and, with
the shower of arrows like hail, the storm of death
sprang up in every direction. To capture lions
eager for battle, the dragon-noose opened its jaws
wide. Through the blue dust the earth became
[coloured] like the sky, with the flash of swords
and helmets for the stars in it. When we overtook
the enemy's squadrons, we dismounted and locked
shield with shield. With arrows and lances we

47

could split a hair, but, lacking good fortune, we had to turn our faces back.

"What force can the grasp of man's effort apply when the arm of God's prospering does not aid? The sword of the malicious was not blunt, because of the malice borne us by our hostile star. Not a man of our army escaped from the fray but his tunic was dabbled with blood. Amongst our men not one pierced even silk with his arrow, of whom I had thought he might have transfixed an anvil with his shaft. Like a hundred grains in an ear of corn we fell, each grain in a different corner. In unmanly fashion we scattered like fish which, though armoured, fall upon the hook. Since the star of our ascendant was on the wane, our shield was as nothing before the arrow of fate."*

One night a gallant warrior could not sleep for a pain in his side. A physician who was near said: " Since he will eat vine-leaves in this fashion I shall be astonished if he survives the night, for it is better to have sharp Tartar arrows in one's breast than to eat unsuitable food. If one morsel causes a griping in his bowel, the fool's whole life will go for nothing."

It happened that the physician died that night. The warrior since then has lived for forty years.†

A rustic's donkey had died and he put its head

* Pp. 288-293.   † P. 295.

as a talisman on a vine in his garden. A wise old man passed that way and, laughing, said to the vineyard-keeper:

" Do not think, my son, that this donkey will ward away the evil eye from your plantation. For this ass could not ward off blows from its own head or buttocks and finally died helpless and miserable."

What does the physician know about removing others' ills, for he must himself die without escape of his ills? *

How well said the poor man in the land of Kish to his ugly wife: " Since the hand of fate has made your face ugly, do not plaster the rouge on it. Who can command fortune by force? Who can restore the blind eye to sight with collyrium? No good deed can come from an evil character; you expect no needlework therefore from dogs, and all the philosophers of Greece and Rome do not know how to obtain honey from a thorn-bush. It never happens that a wild beast turns into a man; and education will, with all your efforts, be wasted on it. One may clean the rust from a mirror, but never can one obtain a mirror from stone. With all one's striving no rose will grow on the willow-tree, nor will an Ethiopian wash white in the bath. Since the arrow of fate cannot be warded off, the slave has no shield except resignation."†

* Pp. 295 f.   † Pp. 297 f.

D o you know the strange tale I brought from Basra—a story sweeter than dates? Some of us, men in the garb of true believers, were passing by a date-garden, when one of our number, whose stomach was a barn and whose belly was ravenous in gluttony, girt up his loins—the unfortunate wretch—and climbed a tree from which he fell heavily on to his head. The village chieftain came and asked who had slain the man. I told him not to raise his voice threateningly against us—" it was his belly plucked his skirts down from the branch. The man of broad guts is narrow hearted. One may not always eat dates and carry them away. This glutton came to a bad end and died. The belly is a fetter for the hand and a shackle for the foot, and a man who is a slave to his belly must be lacking in his service of God. The locust must be all belly, yet the ant of little belly can drag it by the foot."*

A man with a piece of sugar-cane on a tray wandered about hither and thither looking for a purchaser. To a pious man in a village he said:

* Pp. 315 f.

" Take this and pay me when you have the means."

The sage of goodly soul gave him a reply that should be inscribed on one's eyes:

" Though perhaps you may not have to wait for me, I must wait for sugar-cane. Sugar in the cane has no sweetness when there is behind it a bitter demand [for payment]."*

In an old woman's house there was a cat, unfortunate and miserable. It departed once to the amir's palace, where the prince's slaves shot it with arrows. With blood dripping from its bones it fled, saying as it ran in terror of its life: " If I escape from this archer's hands, I and the mouse and the old woman's desolate house will be sufficient. Honey, my soul, is not worth a sting; it is better to be content with one's own date-syrup. God is not pleased with his servant who is not content with the divinely allotted portion."†

The sun of a great and powerful ruler's life was sinking behind the hill. Having no heir to take his place, he bequeathed his realm to a pious elder of the land. Now from the time when that recluse heard the drum of empire he felt no further taste for seclusion from the world; right and left he began to lead his armies and to encourage his warriors. He became so strong of arm and fierce

* P. 316.   † P. 318.

of grip that he sought combat with veterans of battle, and he killed a horde of scattered peoples, the rest of whom gathered together for counsel and support. At last they besieged him so straitly that he was made powerless against the rain of their arrows and stones. To a man of piety, therefore, he sent a messenger to say he was in great distress and to ask for help. " Come to my aid with your piety," he said, " for sword and arrow are not effective in every battle."

When the saint heard the message, he laughed and asked: " Why did he not eat his half-loaf and sleep [content], for the treasure of peace is to be found only in seclusion ?"*

* Pp. 321 f.

ON TRAINING

TAKASH once told his slaves a secret which he forbade them to repeat to anyone. It took a year to travel from his heart to his mouth, and in one day it was spread abroad over the world. He ordered his executioner without delay to cut off the slaves' heads with his sword. But one amongst the victims implored his mercy, and said:

"Slay not your servants, the fault here arose through yourself. You did not stop up [the stream] at the fountain-head; now that it is in spate, of what use is it to bar its passage? Never disclose your heart's secret to any man, for he will repeat it to everyone. Entrust your jewels to your treasury-guards, but watch over your secrets yourself. So long as you have not uttered a word you still have mastery over it, but once it is spoken it gains mastery over you. You know that once a demon has escaped from his bonds, he will not return at anyone's pious conjurations. Words are a captive demon in the dungeon of your heart, do not let it ascend to your palate and tongue. One can allow passage to a vile demon, but by no stratagem can he be brought back."*

Azud had a son who was very ill; and the father's heart could endure it no longer. As an expedient a saintly man bade him release all his wild birds from captivity; whereupon he broke the cages of the birds that sing at dawn. Who would remain captive when the prison is destroyed? But on the roof of his garden-palace he kept a nightingale, famous for its sweet song. The son hastened to the garden at early dawn and found no bird except that one on the palace dome. He laughed and said:

" O nightingale of pleasant voice, through your own utterance you have been left in the cage."

If you utter no word no one can have any plea against you; but once you have spoken, have your arguments ready. Like Sa'dí, who for a time kept his tongue still, and so escaped the attacks of calumniators. That man takes peace of mind to his heart who takes the outside in places where men foregather. Wise man, do not spread men's faults abroad; occupy yourself with your own and leave those of other people alone.†

I have been told that at a feast of drunken slaves an underling broke the minstrel's drum and harp. At once the slaves plucked at his hair as

* Pp. 329 f.   † Pp. 334 f.

though it were a harp, and beat his face as though it were a drum. That night at the pain of the drumming and the beating he could not sleep, and the next day his teacher said in admonition:

" If you do not wish your face to be beaten drum-fashion, keep your head humbly down, my brother, as though you were harping."*

This was the story an old man of wise heart told—pleasantly do the words of the aged strike upon the ear:

Once in India I came upon a corner where I saw a negro, long as mid-winter night. In his arms was a girl as lovely as the full moon, and his teeth were sunk into her lips. So tightly was she held in his embrace you would have thought that night enveloped day. The command anent what was lawful plucked at my skirts, presumption became a fire and I was caught by it. Here and there I looked about for a stick or stone, with which to belabour him, the while I called him godless wretch, infamous and shameless creature. With revilings, abuse, shouts and attacks, like dawn I separated the light from the dark. The lowering cloud departed from over the garden, the white egg appeared from underneath the crow. At the recital of my pious formula the demon form leapt up, while the hand of the fairy-like maiden seized me, and she said:

* P. 335.

" You blue-clad worshipper on hypocrisy's prayer-rug; you evil-doing buyer of worldliness and seller of religion; for whole lifetimes my heart has been lost to this man and my soul has been stirred for him. When the dainty, raw for so long, was at last cooked and ready for me, you snatched it hot from my mouth."

She raised the cry of outrage and called for help, saying that all nobility had fallen to the ground, that compassion was no more and no one was generous enough to come to her rescue.

" Who will obtain justice for me from this old man," she asked, " shameless enough in spite of his old age to put his hand on the veil of a woman unlawful to him? "

She continued her cries, with my cloak gripped in her clutches, while my head sank down into my collar with the disgrace of it. But in a moment I slipped out of my covering like an onion, for I feared the blame of old and young, and I ran naked in front of the woman, in whose hand my cloak was worth more than my person.

Some time later she passed by me and said:

" Do you know me? "

I replied:

" Keep away. Through you I have come to repentance, and no more do I go about officiously. A matter like this does not again occur to a man who wisely sits behind his past deeds. Since that disgraceful act I have found it a piece of

expediency to consider what I see as something
not seen."

Keep your tongue withdrawn, if you have
mind and intellect, speak words like Sa'dí or else
be silent.*

A man sitting in the company of Dáúd of Tayy
said he had seen such and such a Sufi lying drunk
with his turban and shirt defiled, while a crowd
of dogs encircled him. Hearing this report, the
man of blessed spirit frowned at him that brought
it. For a while he remained enraged and then he
said:

" My friend, it is to-day that a compassionate
friend will be of service. Go, remove him from
that vile spot, for what he has done is forbidden
by the Law and is disgraceful in an adept in the
mysteries. Carry him upon your back, for men
who are drunk let go the reins of safety from their
hands."

The hearer became uneasy at the words and was
plunged deep into thought as an ass into the mire,
for he had neither the hardihood to disobey the
Shaykh's command nor the strength to bring back
the drunken man upon his shoulders. For a time
he twisted and writhed, but he saw no remedy nor
any way out of refusing obedience. He girt up his
loins therefore, and, having no choice, he shoul-
dered his friend while the whole town seethed

* Pp. 336-338.

with the story. One reviled the drunkard, calling out:

" Look at the dervish; take warning, ye godly men of pure faith. Behold these Sufis, how they drink wine, pledging their cloaks for drink."

Others pointed their fingers at this man and that, saying:

" This fellow's head hangs heavy," or " That man is half drunk." The enemy's sword at one's throat is preferable to the city's revilings and the ferment of the mob.

Suffering outrage and a period of torment, the man bore his drunken friend to his lodging. That night he could not sleep for shame and thinking, and on the next day Dáúd of Tayy laughed [at him] and said:

" Do not destroy your brother's reputation in a single street, lest fortune destroy your fair fame throughout the whole city."

Speak no ill of any man, good or evil, O generous man, if you are wise; for you make the evil man your enemy and turn the good man into an evil one. When a man tells you that so-and-so is evil, know that he is within the slanderer's own skin; for so-and-so's explanation of his doings is necessary, and demonstration of his evil deed is demanded. Once you have spoken a word of ill against your fellow men, even if what you say is true, you too are evil.

A man once elongated his tongue in slander against an absent person. A sage of noble character said to him:

" Mention no ill of anyone to me, and thereby you will prevent my thinking ill of you. I understand his dignity is diminished, but that fact will never increase the importance of you."

A man once said to me:

" I thought there was a jest which runs that thieving is better than slander? "

I replied:

" O my friend of scattered wits, the saying astonishes me. What good can you see in dishonesty that you give it a higher status than slander? "

" Well," he replied, " thieves show courage, and by the strength of their arms acquire enough for their bellies. What does a fool want with slander; blackening a man's record and deriving no enjoyment from doing so ?"

At the Nizámíya (College) I had a stipend, and night and day I was engaged in instructing and repetition. Once I said to the professor:

" O sage, my colleague so-and-so is jealous of me. If I were to tell the essential truth about him, his vile soul would be destroyed."

The learned principal blazed up in anger and said:

" How wonderful! You do not approve of

your colleague's envy. Who has informed you then that slander is good? If he has gone to hell by the path of meanness, you will overtake him by this other path."*

When I was a child a desire to fast arose within me, though I did not know my right hand from my left. A pious old man in the street showed me, therefore, how to wash my hands and face. Also, he instructed me how I was first to say *Bismilláh* according to the ritual, secondly to compose myself for devotion, thirdly to wash my hands, also to cleanse my mouth and nose three times, to scrape my nostrils with my little finger and rub my front teeth with my forefinger, for it is forbidden when fasting to use a toothbrush after sunset. Then he told me I must pour three handfuls of water on to my face from the place where my hair grew down to my chin, and I was to wash my hands and arms again to the elbow. Now I was to repeat such praises and glorifications as I knew. Then again came the rubbing of my head, followed by the washing of my feet. That ended the lustrations, sealed with the mention of God. Lastly the old man said:

"No one knows this ceremony better than myself. Do you not see how decrepit is the village elder?"

These words came to the ears of the old village chief, and in a rage he said:

* Pp. 338-342.

" O you vile rogue, did you not say it was a sin to use a toothbrush in a fast? Is it lawful, then, to eat the corpses of men? Tell him first to wash his mouth clean of vile words before he washes it clean of food. If a man's name is mentioned in conversation, couple it with the best of honourable qualities. If you constantly repeat that men are asses, do not delude yourself that you will always be reckoned amongst the men. Describe my character abroad as you would speak of it to my face, and if you stand ashamed before the eyes of a beholder, is there not One always present, O sightless one, who knows all that is hidden? Does not shame of yourself come to you that you stand ashamed before me but not before Him? "*

Several men learned in the Mystic Path were sitting in private conclave when one of them began to slander an absent person, and opened the door of speech on that unfortunate fellow. One of the company said to the speaker:

" My friend of untranquil soul, did you ever engage in a raid upon the Franks? " He replied:

" Never in my life have I set foot outside of my own four walls."

" Then indeed," said the dervish of upright soul, " I have not seen anyone so perverse as this man, from whom the infidel sits in security though

* Pp. 343-345.

the Muslim does not escape the injury of his tongue."*

Farídún had a goodly vizier whose mind was clear and his eye far-seeing. God's favour he regarded first, and then he gave heed to the king's command. (The base-born governor does harm to the people, having control of the administration and the increase of the revenue. If you pay no regard to what is due to God, He will bring you to ruin through the king.) A man one morning went to the king and said:

" May every day bring you delight and fortune! Impute no evil motive to me but accept my good counsel. This vizier is secretly your enemy; there is no one great or small in your army who has not borrowed silver or gold from him on condition that it is repaid when your noble majesty dies. That self-regarding minister has no desire for you to live, for fear his money should not come back to him."

The king looked long and with the eye of chastisement upon the vizier, that guardian of the state, then said to him:

" Although you stand in my presence in the guise of a friend, why are you at heart my enemy? "

The minister kissed the ground in obeisance before him, and replied:

* P. 345.

ON TRAINING

" Since you question me I must not conceal the answer. My purpose is, O noble king, that the whole world may desire your welfare as I do. Since your death is the appointed time for the return of my silver, men will the rather wish for your life through their fear of me."*

* Pp. 348 f.

63

ON GRATITUDE

A PRINCE once fell from his black horse and a joint in his neck was dislocated. Like an elephant's, his neck sank down into his frame, so that he could not turn his head without turning his body. The physicians all remained puzzled by it, except a sage from the land of the Greeks, who twisted the prince's head back until the veins ran true. But for him the prince would have been a permanent invalid.

When, on another occasion, the physician came into the presence of the potentate the ingrateful fellow did not cast a glance at him. The sage's head sank in shame, and I heard that as he departed he whispered: " If I had not once turned his neck he would not now be able to turn his face away from me." He sent a seed by the hand of a slave with instructions that he was to burn it in his aloe-burning brazier. The prince sneezed with the smoke of it, and his head and neck once more became as they were.

They sent after the philosopher, making excuses, but though they sought everywhere they did not find him.

Turn not away from gratitude to a benefactor, lest in later days you may not be able to raise your head at all.*

A man, chastising a boy severely, was saying to him:

"You creature of astonishing ideas, you un-blessed one, I gave you an axe to chop wood and not to dig up the wall of the mosque."

The tongue was given for thanks and praise: the grateful man will not use it for backbiting; the ear is the thoroughfare for the Koran and good counsel: make no effort to listen to calumny and falsehood. The eyes are good for beholding the works of God: close them to the faults of brother and friend.†

The night is designed for your delight and the day also, the bright moon and the illuminating sun. For you the morning wind, your slave, spreads out the carpet of spring, and whether there is storm and snow and rain and fog, or whether the thunder hammers with its mallet or the lightning wields its glittering sword, all do it at [God's] command, nourishing also the seed in the ground.

If you are athirst do not rage at your hardship, for the water-carrier of the cloud will bring you water on his back. From the earth He brings forth

* Pp. 376 f.   † Pp. 377 f.

colour and scent and food, entertainment for eye, nose and palate. He gives you honey from the bees, manna from the sky, dates from the palm and the palm from the date-stone. (The date planters bite their hands in astonishment and say: No one ever grew a palm like this.) Sun and moon and Pleiades are all for you, they are the lamps for your palace roof. He produced the rose for you from the thorn and musk from the ox-navel; gold from the mine and fresh leaves from the dry wood. With His own hands He limned your eye and eyebrow, for one's beloved cannot be left to strangers. The All-Powerful who rears the weak feeds them with such varied favours that with every breath and with all one's soul one should thank Him, for it is not a task for tongue alone.

O God! my heart is torn and my eye grieved when I see how much beyond speech are Thy favours. I speak not alone [of the shortcomings] of ravening beasts or tame cattle, or of ant or fish, but also of the ranks of the angels above the zenith of the sky. They all have fallen short in their praise; out of myriads [of miracles] they have spoken but of one thing.

Go, Sa'dí, cleanse your hands and your book too; cease to follow a path that leads nowhere.*

It has been told me that Tughril one night in autumn passed a Hindu watchman, who through

* Pp. 378 f.

the incessant snow and rain and flood had fallen to trembling like twinkling Canopus. Tughril's heart was roused to pity for him, and he said:

" Here is my fur coat, you may put it on. Just wait a moment by the roof, and I will send it out by the hand of a slave."

While he spoke these words, the wind of morning sprang up and the monarch entered his royal palace. Amongst his retinue there he had a slave, beautiful as a peri, for whom he had great affection. The sight of his beloved so pleased him that all thought of the miserable Hindu passed out of his mind. True the words " fur coat " had reached the man's ears, but the thing itself never reached the unfortunate's shoulders. As though the torment of the cold were not enough for him, the turn of Fortune added to it [frustrated] hope. See how the Sultan sleeps without a care and what his guard said in the morning:

" Doubtless Felicitas (the watchman) was forgotten by you when you put your hand to the bosom of Aghúsh (the slave girl). For you the night passed in delight and joy, but do you know how mine passed? "*

Once in Somnáth I saw an ivory idol set with gems, like the image of Manát in the days before Islam. The artist had given it a beauty of form beyond the power of fancy to improve. From

* Pp. 381 f.

every land there came streams of caravans to see the soulless beauty; the kings of China and Chigil, and likewise Sa'dí too, implored the favours of the stony-hearted object. Men of eloquence of every religion made humble supplication before the tongueless object, and at revelation of this sight I was taken aback, wondering why living beings should worship lifeless things. To an idolater who shared my thoughts and doings, one who was my friend, room-mate and companion, I said quietly: " I marvel at what is done in this place where men are distracted by this helpless image and remain bound in the dungeon of error. Its hand has no strength, its foot has not the power to walk, and if you were to throw it down, it could not rise from its place. Can you not see its eyes are made of jewels? Surely it is delusion to pray for good to a thing with eyes of stone."

At my words my friend turned into an enemy. He took fire in his anger and seized me, informing the other idolaters and the elders of the Temple. In the whole assembly I saw not one well-disposed face. The *Pazand*-reading fire-worshippers fell upon me like dogs, because of that bone, for since their crooked way appeared straight to them, the straight path was crooked in their eyes. (Although a man be wise and pious, he may appear an ignoramus to the unlearned.) I was bereft, like a drowning man, of any expedient, seeing no way of escape except dissimulation. When you see a

simpleton in a rage, your safety lies in cajolery
and soft words. Loud, therefore, I flattered the
chief Brahman. " Sage of interpretation and master
of the Zend," I said, " I too admire the carving of
this figure. The form is pleasing and the beauty
of it ravishes the heart. Its beauty is marvellous in
my sight and yet I am without understanding of
its significance, for I am a traveller who has but
recently alighted here; and the foreigner with
difficulty distinguishes the bad from the good.
You understand, you who are the sage of this
territory and the adviser of the king of this land,
what inner meaning lies within the outward form
of this idol, amongst the foremost of whose worshippers I reckon myself. To worship in simple
imitation is to be led astray; oh well, therefore,
for the traveller who knows the path."

The Brahman's face lit up with joy. With approval he said: " O man of acceptable presence,
your question is just, and what you have done is
excellent. He reaches his destination who demands a guide. Like yourself I have wandered
much on my travels and have seen idols unconscious of themselves. But this idol, from the place
where it stands, in the morning raises its hands to
God the Law-giver. If you wish to do so, remain
here to-night, that to-morrow the secret of it may
be revealed to you."

At the old man's behest I remained there
that night, like Bíjhán, a prisoner in the pit of

destruction. The night extended to the length of Judgment Day while the idolaters without lustration stood about me in prayer. The priests touched no water and their armpits stank like corpses in the sun. As though I had committed a grievous sin, I suffered painful torment on that night. The whole night long I was afflicted by the bonds of anxiety, one hand on my heart, the other raised in prayer. Without warning the drummer beat his instrument and suddenly the Brahman called out like a cock. Night, the black-coated preacher, without opposition, drew forth the sword of day from its scabbard. The fire of dawn fell upon tinder, and in a moment the world was kindled. You might have compared it then to the appearance of a [pale] Tartar out of some corner in the land of the negroes. Not a soul, man or woman, remained at home in the city, and in the temple there was no more room even for a needle. I was afflicted by anxiety and drunk with somnolence, when suddenly the image raised its hand. At once from the crowd there arose such a clamour that you would have said it was the sea roused to fury.

When the idol-house was emptied of the throng the Brahman turned smiling to me and said: " I know that you have no difficulties left; the truth has been revealed and all falsehood banished."

I knew then that his ignorance was fixed and that false delusion was firmly implanted within him. I dared not, therefore, say any word of the

truth yet, for the truth must be concealed from
men of falsehood. If you see that the overlord is
a man of brute force, it would not be human
nature to shatter your fist [against him].

For a time I remained hypocritically weeping in
repentance for what I had said, and by my tears
I won the hearts of the infidels. It is not wonderful that the torrent rolls the stone over. The ser-
vitors ran towards me, and with respect took me
by the arm. Uttering excuses I approached the
ivory figure that was seated upon a throne of
beaten gold put on an ebony dais. I kissed the
wretched idol's hand—curses on it and on all
idol-worshippers!—and for a few days I pretended
to become an infidel, and was a Brahman initiated
into the laws of the Zend.

When I saw that I was trusted in the temple, I
could scarce hold myself on the ground for joy.
One night I fastened the temple gate securely, and,
running right and left like a scorpion, I looked
below the dais and above it. I beheld a curtain of
gold embroidery, behind which the arch-priest
and fire-worshipper was seated with the end of
a cord in his hand. At once the matter became
clear to me—like David when the iron became as
wax to him. "It must be," I thought, "that
when he pulls the cord the idol raises its hands in
supplication."

The Brahman was ashamed before me, for the
covering was stripped from his wickedness. He

fled, and I ran after him and flung him headlong
into a well, for I knew that if the Brahman remained alive he would exert all his efforts to slay
me, and would consider it lawful to destroy me
lest I should reveal his secret. When you have
discovered the doings of a villain, make him
powerless if you can; for if you spare the dis-
honourable man's life, he will not desire to see
you alive any longer. And even though he lays
his head down in obeisance at your door, if he
should find power, he will cut off your head. Do
not follow in the footsteps of a treacherous man;
but if you go and you see him, give him no
respite.

I slew the vile wretch outright with a stone, for
no tale comes from a dead man. When I saw that
I had set up a hue and cry, I left that land and fled.
When you have set fire to a reed-bed, you will
beware of the lions [in it] if you are wise. Do not
kill the young of a man-biting snake, but if you
have done so, do not remain in that house. If you
have disturbed a bee-hive, run from that quarter,
for you will be hotly overwhelmed; shoot no
arrow against a man more skilful than yourself;
if it fails, draw up your skirts to your teeth and
flee. In Sa'dí's book there is nothing beyond this
piece of counsel; if you have undermined a wall,
do not stand beneath it.*

* Pp. 388-395.

ON REPENTANCE

O N E night, in our youth and the fullness of our pleasures, a company of us, young men, sat together singing like nightingales, fresh-cheeked as the rose, boldly sending our clamour forth into the street. Sitting apart from us was an old man who had gone about the world, and whose once dark hair had whitened with the hardships of fate. His mouth was closed tight as a nut against words; unlike ourselves, whose mouths were open like the pistachio in laughter. A youth approached the old man and asked why he sat painfully in a corner as though out of envy.

" Raise your head from the collar of grief," the youth said: " let care go, and join in the merriment of the youths here."

The ancient brought his head out of concealment. Behold the answer which, after the fashion of old men, he gave:

" When the wind of morning blows over the rose-garden, it is fitting for the young tree gracefully to bend. So long as the corn is fresh and the ear is green, it bends, but on becoming sere it breaks. In the springtime, when the wind

73

brings the scent of the musk-willow, the old tree
sheds its withered leaves. It would not be fitting
for me to imitate your lively movements, for on
my face the morning of old age has dawned. The
male falcon (my soul), which was fettered within
me, continually wishes to snatch at the end of the
thread of youth. Yours is the time to sit at feasts
like this, for I have washed my hands of pleasure.
When the dust of the years has settled on your
head, look no more for the delights of youth. The
snow has descended on my raven wing; to wander
about the garden no longer befits me. Display is
made by the peacock, who possesses beauty; what
would you from a hawk that has shed its feathers?
For me the time of harvesting my corn draws near.
Your fresh verdure is newly blooming. The
freshness of my rose-garden is past; who will
gather a bunch of roses when they have withered?
I place my reliance now, my son, upon a staff; it
were folly to rely upon life any longer. It is reserved for youth to leap about on its legs; old
men must hold out their hands to implore aid.
Look at the roses of my cheeks, now faded yellow.
When the sun yellows, it sets. For the immature
boy to entertain lusts is not so odious as for the
crude old man to do so. Out of shame for my
sins I must weep as children do, but I cannot live
as a child. Luqmán truly said that it were better
not to live at all than to live one's years sinfully.
Better it is to keep the shop door closed from

dawn than to squander the profits and the capital. While the young man is changing the dark [of his hair] to light, the miserable old man is carrying his whiteness to the grave."*

There were two men between whom there was great enmity and strife, so that each, like a leopard, held his head high against the other in pride. They fled at sight of one another until the very heavens appeared too narrow for them both. Death brought his forces against one of them, and the days of his life came to an end. His enemy's heart rejoiced at that. One day he passed by the grave and saw the tomb-dwelling plastered with clay, though once its occupant's palace had been overlaid with gold. Walking proudly, he came to the head of it and said to himself, his lips open in a smile: "Happy is the tranquillity of the man who, after his enemy's death, finds himself in his friend's embrace. Do not weep for the man who lives, if it be but one day, after the death of his enemy."

Out of enmity and with the arm of violence he tore a plank from the top of the grave. In it he beheld his enemy's head, crowned even in the pit, though his two eyes which had beheld the world were filled with earth. His limbs were captive in the prison of the grave; his body was food for the worm and plunder for the ant. His

* Pp. 399-401.

bones were as tightly packed with dust as the ivory tutty-box is filled with collyrium. By fortune's revolution, the full moon of his face had shrunk to a crescent; through the ravages of time his slim form had become a tooth-pick. As for the hand that once possessed the grip of strength, time had separated it joint from joint. Pity from his very heart overcame him that looked, and from his tears the dust was changed to mire. Repenting of his ugly deeds and feelings, he bade them write on the tombstone: " Rejoice not at anyone's death; for after him no long time remains to you."

A wise saint heard the story, and he cried:

" O mighty Omnipotence; a marvel if thou dost not grant compassion to him over whom his enemy wept. Our body, too, will one day become that over which the enemy's heart grieves. Perhaps compassion for me will come into my friend's heart when he sees that my enemy pardons me."*

A man once ate up the wealth of others by fraud. When (after punishment) he was released, he uttered curses on the devil.

Thus spoke the devil to him on the road:

" Never have I seen a fool to equal you. Between you and me there is an understanding, why then raise your head in hostility against me? It hurts me that the bidding of an ugly demon should

* Pp. 411-414.

76

be written down against you by the hand of an angel. Do you approve, in your ignorance and irreverence, that the pure angels should inscribe your impurities? Look for the path of good and seek peace; set up an intercessor and utter your pleas in excuse for yourself; for not a moment's security can be expected once time's revolution has filled the cup. And if you have not employed your hands according to your powers with works of good, then raise your hands in supplication like any helpless wretch. Then, if your wickedness is beyond measure, you will achieve good if you acknowledge your evil past. Arise when you see the door of pardon open, for the door of repentance may close without warning. Continue not under a load of sin, for the laden man suffers on a journey; and you must hasten in the steps of the saintly, for all that seek this felicity will find it. You, however, are following at the tail of a vile demon; I know not how you will find a place amongst the righteous."*

In San'á a child of mine died. What shall I say of how I suffered? Heaven never drew a picture, even though it were as beautiful as Joseph, which that whale—the grave—did not swallow like Jonah. No cypresses ever grew tall in this garden which the wind of death did not root up. Marvel not if the rose blooms out of his dust, for many a

* Pp. 420 f.

one endowed with rose-like body sleeps in the ground. I said to myself:

" Thou shame of mankind, die; for the child departs pure, but the older man is defiled." Raving and distraught for him, I drew aside the stone from his resting-place, and through terror in that dark and narrow place, I was thrown into perturbation and my whole being suffered a transmutation. But when I recovered my senses after that change of my soul, a voice from my darling son came to my ears: " If terror fall upon you from this dark spot, be wise and enter into the light. Would you have the grave's night illumined like day, then kindle the lamp of good deeds to shine from here. The body of the toiler trembles in a fever lest his palms may not produce dates; many men in avarice fancy that though they have not scattered corn, they will reap a harvest. O Sa'dí, *he* ate the fruit who planted the root; *he* reaps the harvest who scattered the seed."*

* Pp. 431 f.

ON PRAYER

I H A V E heard that a drunken fellow, impelled by wine, ran into the most sacred shrine in a mosque. He wept at the threshold of Mercy: " O God, carry me to the highest heaven." The muezzin seized him by the collar, shouting: " A dog? And in a mosque? You creature bereft of reason and faith! What worthy deed have you done to merit Paradise? Mercy would not become your hideous face."

While the old man spoke these words the drunkard wept: "I am drunk; keep your hand away from me, my master. Are you astonished that a sinner may hope for the grace of the Provider? I do not ask thee, muezzin, to accept my excuses; the door of repentance is open, and God takes me by the hand. I stand in shame before the compassion of the Merciful One when I declare my heavy sins before His pardoning. A man that is prostrated by old age will not rise from where he has fallen unless you take him by the hand. I am that old man prostrated. O God, in your bounty, help me. I say not, grant me greatness and position, pardon the sin that brought me misery and my transgression. If a friend knows of some small fault in me, he proclaims my folly abroad. Thou art the seeing one, and we are fearful of one another; for thou upholdest the veil, and we tear it down.* None has there been with a blacker scroll than myself, for I have done nothing worthy of approval. But relying upon Thy aid I have hope of Thy forgiveness. I have no substance but hope; O God, leave me not without hope of pardon."†

---

* P. 433 omitted.   † Pp. 442-444.

THE GULISTÁN
or
ROSE GARDEN

THE REASON FOR WRITING
THE GULISTÁN

O N E night I was reflecting on the time which had elapsed, and lamenting that so much of my life was spent; I penetrated the stony mansions of my heart with the diamonds of my tears, and repeated the following lines as applicable to my condition:

At every moment of your life a breath is expended, so that what remains is but of small account. Alas! you have spent fifty years in sleep, will you achieve aught in these few days remaining? Shame on that man who departed without finishing his work; who, when the drum was beaten for marching, had not made up his burthen. The sweet sleep of the day of travel holds back the traveller from his way. Every man who ever came erected a new fabric; he departed and evacuated the tenement for another to enter; and he, in like manner, formed new schemes; but no one ever finished the building.

Place no reliance on an unsteady friend; a treacherous man is unworthy of comradeship. The chiefest part of man's life is his belly; so long

81   G

as it depart gradually what cause for woe there-fore? Four opposing and obstinate essences for a few short days dwell happily together; if one of the four should predominate, sweet life departs from amongst them. Of necessity, therefore, a wise and understanding man will not pay over-much regard for the life of this world. Since both the good and the bad must die, happy is that man who carries off the ball of virtue. Send to your own tomb the provisions for the journey; no one will bring them after you, therefore dispatch them before your departure. Life is snow, and the summer sun advanceth: only a small part re-maineth unmelted: art thou yet slothful? You who have gone empty-handed to market, I fear will not return with a full napkin. Whosoever eateth his wheat before it is ripe, must glean ears of corn at the time of harvest. Listen with the ear of your mind to the admonition of Sa'dí; the road is as I have described it; be a man! March!

ON THE WAYS OF KINGS

I HAVE heard that a certain monarch having
commanded a captive to be put to death, the poor
wretch, in a fit of despair, began in his own language to abuse and reproach the king; according
to the saying, " Whosoever washeth his hands of
life, uttereth whatever is in his heart. A man
without hope speaketh boldly; as the cat when
driven to despair seizeth the dog. In the time of
need, when it is impossible to escape, the hand
graspeth the sharp-edged sword." The king asked:
" What doth he say? " One of the viziers, who
was of a benevolent disposition, replied: " O
my Lord," he said, " the Almighty befriendeth
him who stifleth his anger, and is merciful to his
fellow creatures." The king had compassion on
him, and spared his life. Another vizier, of a
contrary temper, said: " It becometh not persons
of our rank to speak anything but truth in the
presence of monarchs; that man reviled the king,
and spoke indecently." The king was displeased
at his speech, and said: " I am more satisfied with
that falsehood than with this truth, which you

83

have uttered; because that was well intended, and this is founded on malignity; and the sages have declared that falsehood mixed with good advice is preferable to truth tending to excite strife." ' When a king is guided by the advice of another, woe be unto him if he speaketh anything but good.' On the portico of the hall of Farídún was written, ' The world, O my brother, continueth not to anyone; place your affections on the Creator of the universe, and that will suffice. Make no reliance, neither rest, upon the kingdom of this world, seeing how many like yourself it hath nourished and then killed. When the pure soul is about to depart, what is the difference between expiring on a throne or on the bare ground? '*

A gang of Arabian robbers had assembled on the top of a mountain, and blocked up the road of the caravan. The inhabitants were distressed by their stratagems, and the troops of the Sultan overpowered; because the thieves, having possessed themselves of a fortress on the summit of the mountain, made this stronghold their fixed residence. The counsellors of the king's party consulted together how to remove this grievance, because if they were suffered to continue any time in this state, they would become too powerful to be subdued. 'The tree that has only just taken root, may be pulled up by the strength

* Tale I.

of a man, but should it continue some time in that state it could not be eradicated even by a windlass. It is possible to stop up the course of a spring with a spade, which when formed into a full stream cannot be forded by an elephant.'

They came to the determination to send one as a spy, to watch the opportunity when the thieves should be gone to attack a tribe, and the place evacuated. They detached a party of battle-tried men who concealed themselves in the pass of the mountains. In the evening, when the robbers returned from their expedition with their plunder, they laid aside their weapons, and deposited their spoil. The first enemy who attacked them was sleep, about the end of the first watch of the night. ' The sun's disc passed into shadow; Jonah entered into the whale's belly.' The gallant men sprang out of the ambush and pinioned the robbers one after another. In the morning they were brought to the palace, when the king gave orders for them all to be put to death.

There happened to be amongst them a lad, the first fruits of whose youth were yet immature; the freshness of his cheeks resembled a rosebud in early spring. One of the viziers kissed the foot of the king's throne, and bowed his head to the earth in intercession, saying, " This boy hath not yet tasted the fruit of the garden of life, nor ever enjoyed the harvest of the season of youth. I therefore venture to hope from your Majesty's known clemency, that you will oblige your servant by sparing the lad's life." The king looked displeased at these words, as they did not accord with his enlightened understanding, and he observed that an evil root will not thrive in a goodly shade. ' To educate the worthless, is like throwing a walnut upon a dome; it is better to eradicate them altogether; for to extinguish the fire and suffer a spark to remain, or to kill the snake and preserve the young, is not acting like a wise man. Though the clouds should pour down the water of life, you would never gather fruit from the branch of the willow. Waste not your time on base people, for we can never obtain sugar from the reed.'

When the vizier heard these words he reluctantly approved of them, and praised the king for his just observation, saying: " May the king live for ever! Nothing can be more true than what my lord hath pronounced, that if he had continued with these wicked wretches he would naturally have fallen into their evil courses, and would have become one of them; but your servant entertains hopes that this boy, by associating with men of probity, will receive instruction and imbibe virtuous sentiments; for being but a child, his principles cannot be tainted with the lawless and inimical disposition of the banditti ; for in the Traditions of the Prophet it is recorded: Of a truth every one is born with a disposition to

86

Islamism, and it is owing to his parents his becoming a Jew, a Christian, or a Magian." 'Lot's
son associated with the wicked, and his posterity
forfeited the gift of prophecy, but the dog of the
[Seven] Sleepers in the cave, by long converse
with the virtuous, became a rational creature.'

The vizier having thus concluded his speech,
some of the courtiers joined in his petition, till at
length the king spared the life of the youth, and
said, " I grant your request, although I disapprove
of it. Know you not what Zál said to Rustam?
Consider not any enemy as weak and contemptible. We have frequently seen water issue from
a small spring, which so increased in its course
that it carried away the camel with his load."

In fine, the vizier took the youth into his family
and educated him with kindness and diligence.
An able master was appointed his tutor, who
taught him how to ask a question and return an
answer with elegance, together with all the accomplishments required for court, so that his
manners met with general approval. Once when
the vizier mentioned to the king some particulars
of the youth's disposition and manners, and was
saying that wise education had made impression
on him, and that his former ignorance was rooted
out of his mind, the king laughed at those ex-
pressions and quoted: ' Thou wast nourished at
our breast and hast grown up amongst us; but
has one ever informed thee that thou art the son

of a wolf. When one's nature is that of a wolf, it will not be benefited by the learning of the scholar. The wolf's whelp will at length become a wolf, although it be brought up along with men.'

A year or two after this conversation, a set of vagabonds of the town entered into a conspiracy with him, and taking an opportunity, he killed the vizier and his two sons, carried off an immense booty, and, succeeding to his father's place in the robber's cave, he became an avowed rebel. The king apprised thereof, in the emotion of amazement, exclaimed: ' How can anyone form a good sword out of bad iron? O ye philosophers, it is impossible to convert a worthless wretch into a good man. The rain, the beneficence of whose nature is beyond dispute, produces tulips in the garden, but only weeds in a barren soil. A sterile soil will not yield spikenard, waste not then the seed of labour upon it. To shew favour to the wicked is, in fact, doing injury to the good.'*

A king was sitting in a ship with a Persian slave. The boy, having never before seen the sea nor experienced the distress of shipboard, began to cry and lament, and his whole body was in a tremor. Notwithstanding all the soothings that were offered, he would not be pacified. The king's diversion was interrupted, and no remedy could

* Tale IV.

be found. A philosopher who was in the ship said:
" If you will command me, I will silence him."
The king replied: " It will be an act of great kindness." The philosopher ordered them to throw
the boy into the sea, and after several plunges
they laid hold of the hair of his head, and dragging
him towards the ship he clung to the rudder with
both his hands.

After a while he sat in a corner of the vessel and
was calmed. The king was pleased, and asked how
this was brought about. The philosopher replied:
"At first he had never experienced the danger of
being drowned; neither knew he the safety of a
ship." In like manner, he knoweth the value of
prosperity who hath encountered adversity. ' O
thou who hast satisfied thine hunger, to thee a
barley loaf is beneath notice; that seems loveliness
to me which in thy sight appears deformity. To
the nymphs of Paradise, Purgatory would be
Hell; but ask the inhabitants of Hell, whether
Purgatory is not Paradise. There is a difference
between him who claspeth his mistress in his
arms, and him whose eyes are fixed on the door
expecting her.'*

I heard of a king who had spent the night in
jollity, and when he was completely intoxicated,
he said: " I have never in my life experienced a
more pleasant moment than the present, for I

* Tale VII.

have no thoughts about good or evil, and am not plagued with anyone." A naked dervish who had been sleeping without in the cold, said: " O King, there is none equal to thee in power—I grant that you have no sorrow of your own, but what then, hast thou no concern about us? " The king was pleased at this speech, and threw out of the window a bag of a thousand dinars, and said: " O dervish, hold out your skirt." He answered: " Whence shall I produce a skirt, who have not a garment? "

The king the more pitied his weak estate, and in addition to the money sent him a dress. The dervish having consumed the whole sum in a short time, came again. ' Riches remain not in the hand of the pious, neither patience on the heart of a lover nor water in a sieve.' At a time when the king had no care about him, they related his case. He was angry and turned away his face from him, and to this point men of wisdom and experience have observed that we ought to guard against the fury and rage of kings, for frequently their thoughts are engrossed by important affairs and they cannot endure interruption from the vulgar. Sometimes they will be enraged at a greeting, and at other times will reward an insult with a robe of honour. ' Whosoever watches not a fit opportunity must expect nothing from the king's favour. Till you perceive a convenient time for conversing, lose not your own consequence by talking to no purpose.' The king said: " Drive away this insolent extravagant fellow, who has dissipated such an immense sum in so short a time; since the Treasury is designed to afford a mouthful for the poor, and not to feast the fraternity of devils." 'The blockhead who burns a camphor candle in the daytime, you will soon see without oil in his lamp at night.' One of the viziers, a good counsellor, said: " O king, it seems expedient that stated allowances should be settled for people of this class separately for their maintenance, that they may not live extravagantly; but what you commanded concerning chiding and excluding them altogether—it would be repugnant to the principles of men of standing to fill one with hopes through kindness, and then to destroy him with despair." ' One cannot admit people into one's presence, and when the door of liberality is open, then shut it upon them with violence. No one seeth the thirsty pilgrims on the seashore; wherever there is a spring of sweet water, men, birds, and ants flock together.'*

A certain vizier, being dismissed from his office, joined a society of dervishes, the blessing of whose company made such an impression as bestowed comfort on his mind. The king was again favourably disposed towards him, and ordered that he should be reinstated; to which the vizier would not consent, saying that degradation was prefer-

* Tale XIII.

able to employment. 'They who are seated in the corner of retirement, close the dog's teeth and men's mouths. They tear up their papers and break their pens, and are delivered from the hands and tongues of slanderers.' The king said: " Of a truth we stand in need of a man of such sufficiency for the administration of our government." The vizier observed that the proof of a man's being sufficiently wise was his not engaging in such matters. ' The phœnix is honoured above all other birds because it feeds on bones, and injures not any living creature.'

They asked a jackal: "Why do you choose the servile society of the lion? " He replied: " Because I eat the remains of his hunting, and live guarded from the machinations of my enemies, under the protection of his valour." They asked: " Now that you are under the shadow of his protection, and gratefully acknowledge his beneficence, why do you not approach nearer, so as to be brought into the circle of his principal servants, and to be numbered amongst his favourite ministers? " He replied: " I am not so confident of my safety from his severity." 'If the Zoroastrian lights the fire an hundred years, yet should he fall into it, for an instant, he would be burnt.' It may happen that a king's minister obtains money; or he may chance to lose his head. The sages have said: " Beware of the inconstant disposition of princes, who sometimes are dissatisfied

at a salutation; and sometimes in return for rude-
ness will bestow a dress of honour." And they
have also observed over-abundant wit is an
accomplishment in a courtier, but a blemish in
the character of a wise man. ' Preserve the dignity of your own character, and leave sport and
buffoonery to courtiers.'*

They have related that Núshírwán, being at a
hunting seat, was about to have some game
dressed, and as there was not any salt, a servant
was sent to fetch some from a village, where the
monarch ordered him to pay the price of the salt
that the exaction might not become a custom and
the village be desolated. They said to him: "From
this trifle, what injury can ensue? " He replied:
" Oppression was brought into the world from
small beginnings, which every new comer has
increased, until it has reached the present degree
of enormity." ' If the monarch were to eat a single
apple from the garden of a peasant, the servants
would pull up the tree by the roots: and if the
Sultan orders half an egg to be taken by force, his
soldiers will spit a thousand fowls. The iniquitous
tyrant remaineth not, but the curses of mankind
rest on him for ever.'†

They tell a story of an oppressor, who flung a
stone at the head of a pious man. The dervish,

* Tales XV and XVI.   † Tale XX.

not having power to revenge himself, kept the stone till a time when the king, being displeased, ordered the other to be thrown into a pit. The dervish then came and bruised the prisoner's head with the stone, upon which he exclaimed: " Who art thou, and why hast thou flung this stone at my head? " He answered:

" I am such a one, and this is the identical stone that on such a day you flung at my head." He proceeded: " Where were you all this time? " The dervish replied: " I was afraid of your dignity; but now that I see you in the pit I consider it a favourable opportunity to avenge myself." ' Whilst the worthless man is in a state of prosperity, the wise think it proper to pay him respect. When you have not a nail sufficiently sharp for tearing, it is prudent not to contend with the wicked. Whosoever grapples against an arm of steel will injure his own wrist, if it is of silver; wait until fortune ties his hands, when to the satisfaction of your friends you may pick out his brains.'*

A certain king had a terrible disease, the nature of which it is not proper to mention. A number of Greek physicians agreed that there was no other remedy for this disease but the gall of a man of some particular description. The king ordered such a one to be sought for, and they found a

* Tale XXII.

94

peasant's son with the properties which the physicians had described. The king sent for the lad's father and mother, and by offering a great reward gained their consent, and the cadi gave his decision that it was lawful to shed the blood of a subject for restoring the health of the monarch. The executioner prepared to put him to death, upon which the youth turned his eyes towards heaven and laughed. The king asked what there could be in his present condition which could possibly excite mirth. He replied: "Children look to their parents for affection; a suit is referred to the cadi; and justice is expected from the monarch. Now my father and mother, deluded by vain worldly considerations, having consented to the shedding of my blood, the judge having sentenced me to die, and the king for the sake of his own health having consented to my death, where am I to seek refuge excepting in God on high? Unto them shall I prefer my suit, since it is from you that I seek justice against you yourself?" The king's heart being troubled at these words, the tears stood in his eyes, and he said: " It is better for me to die than that the blood of an innocent person should be shed." He kissed his head and eyes, and embraced him, and after bestowing considerable gifts set him at liberty. They say, also, that in the same week the king was cured of his distemper. In application to this I recollect the verse which the elephant-driver rehearsed on the banks of the river Nile: 'If you are ignorant of the state of the ant under your foot, know that it resembles your own condition under the foot of the elephant.'*

A person had arrived at the head of his profession in the art of wrestling: he knew three hundred and sixty capital sleights in this art, and every day exhibited something new; but having a sincere regard for a beautiful youth, one of his scholars, he taught him three hundred and fifty-nine sleights, reserving, however, one sleight to himself. The youth excelled so much in skill and in strength that no one was able to cope with him. He at length boasted, before the sultan, that the superiority which he allowed his master to maintain over him was out of respect to his years and the consideration of having been his instructor; for otherwise he was not inferior in strength, and was his equal in point of skill. The king did not approve of this disrespectful conduct, and commanded that there should be a trial of skill.

An extensive spot was appointed for the occasion. The ministers of state and other grandees of the court were in attendance. The youth, like a lustful elephant, entered with a percussion that would have removed from its base a mountain of iron. The master, being sensible that the youth

* Tale XXIII.

was his superior in strength, attacked with the sleight which he had kept to himself. The youth not being able to repel it, the master with both hands lifted him from the ground, and raising him over his head, flung him on the earth. The multitude shouted; the king commanded that a dress and a reward in money should be bestowed on the master, and reproved and derided the youth for having presumed to put himself in competition with his benefactor, and for having failed in the attempt. He said: " O King, my master did not gain the victory over me through strength or skill; but there remained a small part in the art of wrestling which he had withheld from me, and by that small feint he got the better of me." The master observed: " I reserved it for such an occasion as the present; the sages having said, ' Put not yourself so much in the power of your friend that if he should be disposed to be inimical he may be able to effect his purpose.' Have you not heard what was said by a person who had suffered injury from one whom he had educated? ' Either there never was any gratitude in the world, or else no one at this time practises it. I never taught anyone the art of archery who in the end did not make a butt of me.' "

A certain traveller, as he twisted his ringlets, pretended he was a descendant of Ali; and entering the city along with the caravan from Hejaz, said he was a pilgrim from Mecca, and presented the king with an elegy as his own composition. One of the courtiers, who in that year had returned from a journey, said: " I saw this man at the time of the festival of sacrifice [celebrated by pilgrims at Mecca] at Basra; how then can he be a Hâjji?" Another said: " His father is a Christian at Malatiya; how then can he be of the sacred stock?" And they discovered his verses in the diwan of Anwarí. The king ordered that he should be punished and driven away, and asked him why he had uttered such falsehoods. He replied: " O King of the earth, I will speak one word more, and if it should not be true I shall deserve any punishment that you may command." The king asked: " What is that? " He replied: " If a peasant brings you curds, two parts of it are water and one spoonful is sour milk; be not therefore offended if your slave should have uttered an inconsiderate speech, for a traveller tells many lies." The king laughed and said he had never made a truer speech in his life, and ordered that what he had asked should be granted.*

Harun al-Rashid, when he had completed the conquest of Egypt, said: " As a contrast to that rebel who through the pride of his possessing the kingdom of Egypt boasted that he was God, I will bestow this kingdom on the meanest of my

* Tale XXXIII.

slaves." He had an Ethiopian slave, named Khosaib, to whom he gave the kingdom. They say that this man's wisdom and knowledge were of such kind that when some of the farmers of Egypt were complaining that an unseasonable fall of rain had destroyed the cotton, which they had sown on the banks of the Nile, he said they ought to sow wool, which would not be destroyed. A man of discernment, upon hearing this, said: ' If the augmentation of wealth depended upon knowledge, none would be so distressed as an ignorant fellow; but God bestows on a single fool as much wealth as would astonish a hundred men of wisdom. Wealth and power depend not upon skill, and cannot be obtained without the assistance of Heaven. It often happens in the world that the imprudent are honoured and the wise are despised. The alchemist died of grief and distress, whilst the blockhead found treasure under a ruin.'*

* Tale XL.

A T H I E F got into the house of a religious man, but after the most diligent search had the mortification not to find anything. The good man, discovering his situation, threw the blanket on which he had slept in the way which the thief had to pass, in order that he might not be disappointed. ' I have heard that those who are truly pious distress not the hearts of their enemies. How canst thou attain to this dignity, who art in strife and contention with thy friends? ' The affection of the righteous is the same in presence as in absence; not like those who censure you behind your back, but before your face are ready to die for you. ' When you are present, meek as a lamb; but when absent, like the wolf, a devourer of mankind.' ' Whosoever recounts to you the faults of your neighbour will doubtless expose your defects to others.'*

Some travellers were journeying together, partakers of each other's cares and comforts. I wanted

* Tale IV.

to associate myself with them, to which they would not consent. I remarked that it was inconsistent with the benevolent manners of religious men to turn away their faces from the poor, and to deny them the advantage of such company; that I knew myself to possess such a degree of energy as would make me an active friend and not an encumbrance to them. 'Although I am not mounted on a beast, I will endeavour to carry your burdens.' One amongst them said: " Be not unhappy at the words which you have heard, for not long ago a thief, under the appearance of a dervish, got into our company. As the condition of a dervish is everywhere approved, they did not entertain any suspicion of his sanctity, but admitted him into their society. ' How can one man know what is under another's garment. The writer [alone] knows the contents of the letter.' ' The exterior of religious men is their dervish's dress. This is sufficient amongst mortals, who look only at the face: let your actions be good, and put on any dress you choose; either wear a crown on your head, or carry a flag on your shoulders. Be truly pious and dress in satin. Sanctity consists in forsaking the world, with its lusts and appetites, not merely in changing the dress. In warfare manhood is required; of what use would armour be to an hermaphrodite? '

To cut my story short: one day we had travelled until dark, and during the night slept at the foot of a castle; the graceless thief, under pretence of going to perform his ablutions, carried off the waterpot of one of his companions, and then went in quest of plunder.

'Behold this person, who covered his body with a religious dress, made the veil of the Ka'ba a housing for an ass.' As soon as he had got out of sight of the dervishes he went on a little way and stole a casket. By the time it was daylight, the dark-minded wretch had gone a great distance; and in the morning his innocent companions (whom he had left asleep) were all carried to the castle, and committed to prison. From that day we resolved not to increase our company, but henceforward to lead the lives of recluses; because in solitude there is tranquility. 'When one of any tribe commits an act of folly, there is no distinction between high and low, the whole being dishonoured. Have you not observed that a single ox belonging to a herd will contaminate all the oxen of the village?' "

I replied: " Thanks to the God of majesty and glory I am not destitute of the benefits which are enjoyed by the religious, although I am separated from their company; for I have derived instruction from this story, which will serve men of our character for admonition during the remainder of life."

'By the means of one disorderly person in a company, the hearts of many wise men become afflicted. If you fill a cistern with rose water, and a dog should fall into it, it would thereby become impure.'*

In the great mosque at Baalbek I was reciting some words by way of admonition to a company whose hearts were withered and dead, incapable of applying the ways of the visible to the purposes of the invisible world. I perceived that what I was saying had no effect on them, and that the fire of my piety had not kindled their green wood. I became weary of instructing brutes, and of holding a mirror in the way of the blind; but the door of signification continued open, and the concatenation of discourse was extended in explanation of this verse of the Koran: " We are nearer to him than his jugular vein." My discourse had got to such a length that I said: ' A friend is nearer to me than myself; but what is more wonderful, I am far from him. What shall I do, to whom shall I address myself, since he is in my arms, whilst I am separated from him?' I was intoxicated with the wine of this discourse, and the dregs of the cup were in my hand when a traveller, passing suddenly by the company, was so much animated by my last words, that he shouted out with an emphasis that produced the acclamations of the whole, and the senseless company joined in enthusiastic rapture. I said: ' O God, those who are

* Tale V.

103

afar off know Thee, whilst those who are near and ignorant are at a distance.' When the hearer does not understand the discourse, expect not any effect of genius from the orator: first have a wide field of eagerness, then the orator may strike the ball of eloquence.*

One night in the desert of Mecca, from great want of sleep, I was deprived of all power to stir. I reclined my head on the earth, and desired the camel-driver not to disturb me. ' How far shall the feet of the poor man proceed when the camel is weary of his load? Whilst the body of the fat man is becoming lean, the lean man may die of fatigue.' He replied: " O brother, Mecca is in front, and robbers in the rear. By proceeding you escape; and if you sleep you die." 'It is pleasant to sleep on the road in the desert under the acacia-tree in the night of travel, but you must consider it as abandoning life.'†

Notwithstanding all that was said to me by the mighty Shaykh Abú'l Faraj Shamsu 'l Dín ibn Jawzí, who ordered me to forsake music meetings and to lead a life of retirement—the desire of sensual gratification not admitting of restraint—in contradiction to the advice of my patron, I abandoned myself to the enjoyments of singing and of the convivial society of dervishes. When

* Tale X.   † Tale XI.

the Shaykh's advice occurred to my recollection, I used to say: ' If the cadi were of our party, he would rub his hands together in rapture; if the censor would drink wine, he would excuse him who is intoxicated.' One night I entered into the society of a tribe, amongst whom was a minstrel of whom you would say that the sound of his bow would break the arteries, and his voice was more horrid than the lamentations of a man for the death of his father.' Sometimes the audience put their fingers into their ears, that they might not hear him, and sometimes they placed their fingers on their lips as a signal for him to be silent. As the Arab says: ' The heart may be captivated by the sound of sweet melody, but such a singer as thou art can only give delight by being silent.' ' No one will experience pleasure from your singing, excepting at the time of your departure, when you stop your breath.' ' When this minstrel began singing, I said to the master of the house: " For God's sake put cotton into my ears, that I may not hear; or else open the door, that I may escape." ' In short, out of regard for the dervishes I accommodated myself to their inclination, and with great effort passed the night until daybreak. ' The muezzin proclaimed prayers out of season, not knowing how much of the night had elapsed. Ask the length of the night from my eyelids, which have not been closed a single moment.'

In the morning, by way of benediction, I took

the turban from my head, and my dirhams out of
my girdle, and presenting them to the singer, I
embraced him, and returned him many thanks.
My companions, seeing me behave towards him
in so unusual a manner, imputed it to weakness of
understanding, and laughed within themselves.
One of them extended the tongue of opposition,
and began reprimanding me, saying: " In this
matter you have not acted as becometh a wise
man, to have given part of your professional dress
to a singer, who during his whole life never at
one time had a dirham in his hand, nor ever saw
a particle of gold on his drum." ' Such a singer
(far may he remain from this happy mansion) no
one ever saw twice in the same place. Of a truth,
when the sound came out of his mouth, it made
men's hair stand on end. The sparrow flies away
from the dread of him; he distracts our intellects,
and tears his own throat.' I answered: " You
should stop your railing, because this man's
miraculous talents have become obvious to me."
He replied: " Explain this discovery in order that
we may unite with you, and ask pardon of him for
the ridicule which has passed." I replied: " My
shaykh has repeatedly enjoined me not to frequent
singing parties, and has given me many admon-
itions to which I have paid no attention until this
night, when the star of auspiciousness and good
fortune guided me to this house where, because
of this singer, I have made a vow never again

to approach singing or convivial parties." 'A pleasant voice from a sweet palate, mouth and lips, whether tempered with musical art or not, captivates the heart; but the musical modes of [the composers] Ushaq, Muhawand and Iraq from the windpipe of a contemptible minstrel, are disgusting.'*

They tell a story of a certain religious man who in one night would eat ten pounds of food, and who, before the morning, would have completely finished the Koran in his devotions. A holy man hearing this, said: " If he had eaten half a loaf, and slept, it would have been much more meritorious." ' Keep your belly unencumbered with food, in order that you may be able to discern the light of divine knowledge. You are void of wisdom, because you are crammed up to your nose with food.'†

They asked one of the Shaykhs of Damascus what was the condition of the sect of Sufis. He replied: " They formerly were, in the world, a society of men apparently in distress, but in reality contented; but now they are a tribe in appearance satisfied, but inwardly discontented."
' When your heart is continually wandering from one place to another, you will have no satisfaction in solitude. Though you possess

* Tale XIX.   † Tale XXI.

riches, rank, lands and chattels, if your heart is with God you are a recluse.'*

Once I travelled to Hejaz along with some young men of virtuous disposition who had been my intimate friends and constant companions. Frequently they sang and frequently they recited spiritual verses. There happened to be in the party a pious man, who thought unfavourably of the morals of dervishes, being ignorant of their sufferings. At length we arrived at the grove of palm trees of Bani Hilal, when a boy came out of one of the Arab families, and sang in such a strain as arrested the birds in their flight in the air, I beheld the pious man's camel dancing, and after flinging his rider he took the road of the desert. I said: " O Shaykh, those strains delighted the brutes, but made no impression on you." ' Knowest thou what the nightingale of the morning said to me? What kind of a man art thou, who art ignorant of love? The camel is thrown into ecstasy by the Arabic verses, for which, if thou hast no relish, thou art a cross-grained brute.' ' The wind blowing over the plains causes the tender branches of the ben-tree to bend before it, but affects not the hard stone.' ' Everything that you behold is exclaiming the praises of God, as is well known unto the understanding heart. Not only the nightingale and the rose-bush are chant-

* Tale XXIV.

ing praises to God, but every thorn is a tongue to extol Him.'*

A certain king, when arrived at the end of his days, having no heir, directed in his will that in the morning after his death the first person who entered the gate of the city they should place on his head the crown of royalty, and commit to his charge the government of the kingdom. It happened that the first person who entered the city gate was a beggar, who all his life had collected scraps of victuals, and sewed patch upon patch. The ministers of state and the nobles of the court carried into execution the king's will, bestowing on him the keys of the fortresses and treasuries. For some time the dervish governed the kingdom, until part of the nobility swerved their necks from his obedience, and all the surrounding monarchs, engaging in hostile confederacies, attacked him with their armies. In short, the troops and peasantry were thrown into confusion, and he lost the possession of some territories. The dervish was distressed at these events, when an old friend who had been his companion in the days of poverty returned from a journey, and finding him in such an exalted state, said: " Praised be the God of excellence and glory, that your high fortune has aided you, and prosperity been your guide, so that a rose has issued from the brier;

* Tale XXVI.

and the thorn has been extracted from your foot, and you have arrived at this dignity. Of a truth, joy succeeds sorrow." ' The bud sometimes blossoms, and sometimes withers; the tree is sometimes naked and sometimes clothed.' He replied: " O brother, condole with me, for this is not a time for congratulation. When you saw me last, I was only anxious how to obtain bread; but now I have all the cares of the world to encounter." ' If the times are adverse, I am in pain; and if they are prosperous, I am captivated with worldly enjoyments. There is no calamity greater than worldly affairs, because they distress the heart in prosperity as well as in adversity.' ' If you want riches, seek only for contentment, which is inestimable wealth. If the rich man should throw money into your lap consider yourself not obliged to him; for I have often heard it said by pious men that the patience of the poor is preferable to the liberality of the rich.' ' If Bahram should roast an onager to be distributed amongst the people, it would not be equal to the leg of a locust to an ant.'*

Having become weary of my friends at Damascus, I retired into the desert near Jerusalem, and associated with the brutes till I was taken prisoner by the Franks and consigned to a pit in Tripoli to dig clay along with some Jews. But one of the

* Tale XXVII.

principal men of Aleppo, with whom I had formerly been intimate, happening to pass that way, recollected me, asked me how I came there, and in what manner I spent my time. I answered: ' I fled into the mountains and deserts to avoid mankind, seeing on God alone reliance can be placed. Conjecture then what must now be my situation, forced to associate with wretches worse than men.' ' To have our feet bound with chains in company with our friends is preferable to living in a garden with strangers.' He then had compassion on my condition, redeemed me for ten dinars from the Franks, and took me with him to Aleppo. He had a daughter whom he gave me in marriage, with a hundred dinars for her dower. When some time had elapsed she discovered her disposition, which was ill-natured, quarrelsome, obstinate and abusive, so that she destroyed my happiness. ' A bad woman in the house of a good man is his hell in this world. Take care how you connect yourself with a bad woman. Defend us, O Lord, from this fiery trial!' Once she reproached me, saying: " Art thou not he whom my father redeemed from captivity amongst the Franks for ten dinars?" I answered: " Yes, he ransomed me for ten dinars and put me into your hands for a hundred."

' I have heard that a certain great man delivered a sheep from the teeth and claws of a wolf, and the night following applied a knife to his throat.

The expiring sheep complained of him, saying:
" You delivered me from the claws of a wolf, but
I have seen you, at length, act the part of the
very wolf towards me." '*

A pupil complained to his spiritual guide of
being much disturbed by impertinent visitors,
who broke in on his valuable time [and he asked
how he could get rid of them]. The superior replied: " To such of them as are poor, lend money;
and from those that are rich ask something, when
you may depend upon not seeing one of them
again." ' If a beggar were the leader of the army
of Islamism, the infidels would flee to China
through fear of his importunity.'†

A lawyer said to his father: " Those fine
speeches of the declaimers make no impression
on me, because I do not see that their actions
correspond with their precepts. ' They teach
people to forsake the world, whilst themselves
accumulate silver and herds.' ' A wise man who
preaches without practising will not impress
others. That person is wise who abstaineth from
sin, not he who teacheth good to others whilst
himself committeth evil. The wise man who in-
dulges in sensual gratifications, being himself
bewildered, how can he guide others?'" The father
replied: " O my son, you ought not, merely from

* Tale XXXI.   † Tale XXXVII.

this vain opinion, to reject the doctrines of the preachers, thus pursuing the paths of vanity by imputing errors to the learned. Whilst you are searching for an immaculate teacher you are deprived of the benefits of learning, like the blind man, who one night, falling into the mud, cried out: ' O Moslems, bring a lamp to show me the way.' An impudent woman who heard him, said: ' You cannot see a lamp, what then can it show you? ' Moreover, the society of the preacher resembles the shop of a trader, where, until you pay money, you cannot carry away the goods; and here, unless you come with good inclination, you will not derive any benefit." ' Listen to the discourse of the learned man with the utmost attention, although his actions may not correspond with his doctrine. It is a futile objection of gainsayers that " how can he who is asleep awaken others? " It behoveth a man to receive instruction although the advice be written on a wall.'

'A certain holy man, having quitted a monastery and the society of religious men, became a member of a college. I asked what was the difference between being a learned or a religious man, that could induce him to change his society. He replied: " The devotee saves his own blanket out of the waves, and the learned man endeavours to rescue others from drowning." '*

* Tale XXXVIII.

'Attend to the following story: In the city of Baghdad there happened a contention between the flag and the curtain. The flag, disgusted with the dust of the road and the fatigue of marching, said to the curtain in displeasure: " You and myself are schoolfellows, both servants of the Sultan's court. I never enjoy a moment's relaxation from business, being obliged to travel at all seasons. You have not experienced the fatigue of marching, the danger of storming the fortress, the perils of the desert, nor the inconveniences of whirlwinds and dust. My foot is more forward in enterprise; why then is thy dignity greater than mine? You pass your time amongst youths, beautiful as the moon, and with virgins odoriferous as jasmine. I am carried in the hands of menial servants, and travel with my feet in bands, and my head agitated by the wind." The curtain replied: " My head is placed on the threshold, and not, like yours, raised up to the sky. Whosoever through folly exalts his neck precipitates himself into distress." '*

' A merry fellow of Baghdad married his daughter to a shoemaker. The little man, having a flinty heart, bit the girl's lips in such a manner that they trickled with blood. In the morning, her father, beholding her in such plight, went to his son-in-law, and said to him: " O you worthless

* Tale XLI.

fellow, what kind of teeth have you got thus to chew her lips, as if they were made of leather? I am not speaking in jest. Leave off your jokes and have your legal enjoyment. When bad manners become habitual, they cannot be got rid of until death." '*

* Tale XLIV.

ON THE EXCELLENCY OF
CONTENTMENT

O N E of the kings of Persia sent a skilful physician to Mustafa (Mohammed), upon whom be
peace! He (the physician) had been some years in
Arabia without anyone having come to make
trial of his skill, neither had they applied to him
for any medicine. One day he came to the prince
of prophets and complained, saying: " They sent
me to dispense medicines to your companions,
but to this day no one hath taken notice of me
that I might have an opportunity of performing
the service to which I had been appointed."
Mohammed replied: " It is a rule with these
people never to eat until they are hard pressed by
hunger; and to leave off eating whilst they still
have a good appetite." The physician said: " That
is the way to enjoy health." He then made his
obeisance and departed. ' The physician begins to
speak or to stretch out his finger towards viands
only when evil would result from his silence, or
when death might ensue from too much abstinence. Then doubtless his speech is wisdom, and
such a meal will be productive of health.'*

* Tale IV.

Two dervishes of Khorasan, who had entered into strict intimacy, travelled together. One who was infirm would fast for two days, and the other, who was robust, used to eat three times a day. It happened that they were seized at the gate of a city on suspicion of being spies, were both confined in the same room, and the door closed up with mud. After a fortnight it was discovered that they were innocent. On opening the door they found the strong man dead and the infirm one alive. They were astonished at the circumstance; but a philosopher said that the contrary would have been more wonderful, for the one who was a greater eater was not able to support abstinence, and the other, who was weak, having his body in subjection and being used to fasting, had happily escaped. 'A person who has accustomed himself to eat sparingly, when difficulty occurs bears it easily; but if in time of prosperity he has been used to pamper himself, when he meets with distress he sinks under it.' 'To stoke the belly continuously means distress on the day when fuel is lacking.'*

They asked a sick man what his heart desired. He replied: "Only this, that it may not desire anything." 'When the stomach is oppressed and the belly suffering pain, there is no benefit even in having all other matters in perfection.'†

* Tale VI.   † Tale VIII.

A certain gallant man was grievously wounded in an expedition against the Tartars. Somebody said: " A merchant has an unguent, of which perhaps he might give you a little were you to ask it." The merchant was notorious for his parsimony. ' If the sun had been on his table instead of bread, no one would have seen light in the world until the Day of Judgment.' The gallant man replied: " If I ask for the unguent it is uncertain whether he will give it or not, and if he should give it, the effect is doubtful. On every account, to ask of such a man is a deadly poison."

' That which you obtain by entreaty from mean people may benefit the body, but it injures the soul.' The sages have said: if the water of immortality, for example, were to be sold in exchange for reputation, the wise man would not purchase it, for an honourable death is preferable to a disgraceful life. ' If you eat colocynth from the hand of a kind man, it is preferable to a sweetmeat given by one who has a crabbed countenance.'*

I never complained of the vicissitudes of fortune, nor murmured at the ordinances of heaven, excepting once, when my feet were bare and I had not the means of procuring myself shoes. I entered the great mosque at Cufah with a heavy heart, when I beheld a man who had no feet. I offered up praise and thanksgiving to God for

* Tale IX.

His bounty, and bore with patience the want of shoes. ' A broiled fowl, in the eyes of one who has satisfied his appetite, is of less estimation than a leaf of greens on a dish; but to him who hath not the means of procuring food, a boiled turnip is equal to a boiled fowl.'*

I saw a merchant who possessed one hundred and fifty camels laden with merchandise, and forty slaves. One night, in the island of Kish, he entertained me in his own apartment, and during the whole night did not cease talking in rambling fashion, saying: " I have such and such a partner in Turkistan, and such goods in Hindustan; these are the title-deeds of such and such a piece of ground, and, for this matter, such a one is security." Sometimes he would say: " I have an inclination to go to Alexandria, the air of which is very pleasant." Then again: " No, I will not go, because the Mediterranean sea is boisterous. O Sa'dí, I have another journey in contemplation, and after I have performed that I will pass the remainder of my life in retirement, and leave off trading." I asked what journey it was. He replied: " I want to carry Persian brimstone to China, where I have heard it bears a very high price; from thence I will transport China ware to Greece, and take the brocades of Greece to India, and Indian steel to Aleppo. The glass-ware of Aleppo

* Tale XVIII.

I will convey to Yemen, and from thence go with striped cloths to Persia; after which I will leave off trade and sit down in my shop." He spoke so much of this foolishness that at length, being quite exhausted, he said: " O Saʻdí, relate also something of what you have seen and heard." I replied: " Have you not heard that once upon a time a merchant, as he was travelling in the desert, fell from his camel. He said that the covetous eye of the worldly man is either satisfied through contentment or will be filled with the earth of the grave."*

I heard of a certain rich man, who was as notorious for parsimony as Hátim of Tayy for liberality. His external form was adorned with wealth, but the meanness of his disposition was so rooted that he never gave even a loaf of bread to anyone; he would not have bestowed a scrap on the cat of Abu Huraira,† nor throw a bone to the dog of the Seven Sleepers. In short, no one ever saw his door open nor his table spread. ' A poor man never knew his victuals, excepting by the smell; no bird ever picked up any crumbs that fell from his table.' I heard that he was sailing on the Mediterranean sea towards Egypt, with all the pride of Pharaoh in his imagination. Suddenly a contrary wind assailed the ship so that the sea

* Tale XXI.
† The Prophet's companion, who had a pet cat.

was lashed to turmoil, until drowning overtook him.

'What can the heart do when something does not accord with your sorrowful disposition? The north wind is not always favourable for the ship.' He lifted up the hands of imploration, and uttered ineffectual lamentations. (And when they embarked in ships they called upon God, calling their faith pure before Him.)*

'Of what benefit will it be to the servant in the time of need to lift up his hands in imploration which are extended during prayers, but when any favour is wanted are folded under his arms?' 'Bestow comfort on others with silver and gold, and from thence derive also benefit yourself. Then this edifice of yours will remain; use, therefore, bricks of gold and bricks of silver.'

They have related that he had poor relations in Egypt, who were enriched with the remainder of his wealth. At his death they rent their garments and made up silk and damasks. In that same week I saw one of them riding a fleet horse with an angelic youth running after him, and to myself I said: "Alas, if the dead man should return amongst his tribe and relations, the heirs would feel more sorrow in restoring him his estate than they suffered on account of his death." On the strength of the acquaintance which had formerly subsisted between us, I pulled his sleeve, and said:

* Koran.

" Enjoy thou, O good man of happy endowments, that wealth which the late possessor accumulated to no purpose."*

A thief said to a mendicant: " Are you not ashamed to hold out your hand to every sordid wretch to obtain a grain of silver? " He replied: ' It is better to stretch out the hand for a grain of silver than to have it cut off for having stolen an obol and a half.'†

They tell a story of a wrestler, who, from adverse fortune, was reduced to the extremity of misery. With a craving appetite and destitute of the means of subsistence, he came complaining to his father, and requested leave to travel, if perchance by the strength of his arm he might be able to accomplish his wishes. ' Talents and skill are of no value without being exhibited; they put aloes on the fire, and grind musk.' The father said: " O son, get out of your head impracticable imaginations, and draw back the foot of contentment within the skirt of safety, for the sages have said riches are not to be obtained by bodily exertion, but the remedy against want is to moderate our desires." ' No one can seize the skirt of wealth by force, it is lost labour to anoint the eyes of the blind with salve.'

' If every hair of your head possessed two hun-

* Tale XXII.   † Tale XXVI.

dred accomplishments, they would be of no use when fortune is unpropitious.' 'What can a strong but unfortunate man do? The arm of fortune is better than the arm of strength.' The son said: " O father, the advantages of travelling are many, and its benefits innumerable: the recreation of the mind, profitable attainments, to see wonders and to hear strange things, the view of cities, the conversation of mankind, the acquisition of honour, the attainment of knowledge and manners, the increase of wealth, the means of gaining a livelihood, forming intimate connections, and the experience of the world. As has been observed by men of piety: ' As long as you stick to your shop and to your house, never, O simpleton, will you become a man. Go and travel over the world before the time shall arrive for your quitting it.' "

The father made answer: " O son, the advantages of travelling in the manner that you have set forth are doubtless very great; but it is most fitting for five classes of men: first the merchant, who, possessing wealth and dignity, with beautiful slaves and handmaids and active servants, may pass every day in a new city and every night in a different place, and may every minute in delightful spots recreate himself with worldly luxuries. The rich man is not a stranger, neither in the mountains nor in the deserts: wherever he goes he pitches his tent and takes up his quarters;

whilst he who possesses not the comforts of life, but is destitute of the means of supporting himself, is a stranger, and unknown even in his native country. Secondly, a learned man, who on account of his sweet speeches, powerful eloquence and store of knowledge, wherever he goes is universally sought after and respected. ' The presence of a wise man resembles pure gold, because whithersoever he goeth they know his value and consequence.' An ignorant son of a rich man is like leather-money, passing current in a particular city, but which in a foreign country no one will receive for anything. Thirdly, the beautiful person to whom the hearts of the virtuous are inclined. According to the saying, a little beauty is preferable to great wealth. A beautiful person is the balm for a wounded heart and is the key of the locked door. Therefore they set a high value on his company and consider it an honour to do him service. ' The beautiful person, wheresoever he goes, meets with honour and respect, even if his father and mother should turn him out with displeasure. I saw a peacock's feather in the leaves of a Koran. I said: " I consider this an honour much greater than your quality deserves." It replied: " Be silent; for whosoever has beauty, wherever he puts his foot, doth not everyone receive him with respect?" The son who is endowed with elegance and beauty careth not for his father's anger. If he is a rare pearl, let him not remain in the parent shell; of a precious pearl everyone will be the purchaser.' Fourthly, a sweet singer, who with the throat of David arrests the waters in their course, and suspends the birds in their flight; consequently, by the power of this perfection, he captivates the hearts of mankind in general, and the religious are desirous of associating with him. 'My attention is engaged in listening to a sweet voice: Who is this beautiful person playing on the double chord?' 'How delightful is a tender and plaintive voice at the dawn of day, in the ears of those intoxicated with love! A sweet voice is better than a beautiful face; for the one gives sensual delight, and the other invigorates the soul.' Fifthly, the craftsman, who gains subsistence by the labour of his arm, that his good name may not be disgraced by the want of bread. According to this saying of the wise: 'If a craftsman goes a journey from his own city, he suffers not difficulty nor distress, but if the king of Nímrúz should wander out of his kingdom, he would sleep hungry.' The aforementioned qualities which I have explained are the means of affording comfort to the mind in travelling, and are the bestowers of sweet delight; but he who does not possess them will enter the world with vain expectations; and no one will hear his name, nor see any signs of him. ' Whomsoever the revolutions of Heaven in malice afflict, the world betrays. The pigeon who is not to see his nest again, fate conducts to the grain and snare.'"

The son said: " O father, how can I contradict another maxim of the sages, which says the necessaries of life are distributed to all, yet the attainment thereof requires exertion, and although misfortune is decreed, it is our duty to shun the way by which it enters?

'Although our daily bread doubtless may come to us, yet reason requires that we should seek it out of doors. Although no one can die before it is decreed by fate, you have no occasion to run into the jaws of the dragon.'

In my present situation I am able to encounter a furious elephant and to combat a devouring lion; and I have besides this inducement to travel, that I am no longer able to suffer indigence.

' When a man falls from his rank and dignity, what has he more to concern himself about? He is a citizen of the world. A rich man repairs at night to his palace, but wheresoever the dervish is overtaken by night, that place is his inn.'"

This he said, took leave of his father, asked his blessing, and departed. At his departure he was heard to say: ' The artist to whom fortune is not propitious goeth to a place where his name is not known.' He travelled until he arrived on the banks of a river, so rapid that the stones dashed against stones, and the noise was heard at many miles distance. It was a tremendous water in which even waterfowls were not in safety, and the smallest of its waves would impel a millstone from the shore. He saw a number of people sitting at the ferry, each of whom had a small piece of money. The young man, having no money, used supplications, but without effect. The inhuman boatman laughed at him and turned away, saying: " If you have no money you cannot here commit violence on anyone, and if you have money there is no need of force. You have no money and you cannot cross the river by means of your strength. Of what avail is the strength of ten men? Bring the money of one." The young man, incensed at this sarcasm, wished to be revenged on him. The boat had put off. He called out: " If you will be satisfied with this garment which I have on my back, I will freely give it to you." The boatman, being greedy, brought back the boat. ' Covetousness sews up the eyes of the cunning and covetousness brings both bird and fish into the net.' As soon as the young man's hands were in reach of the boatman's beard and collar, he dragged him towards him and knocked him down without ceremony. One of his comrades stepped out of the boat to help him, but experienced such rough treatment that he desisted. They both thought it advisable to pacify the young man, and compromised with him for the fare. ' When you see fighting, be peaceable, for a peaceable disposition shuts the door of contention. Oppose kindness to perverseness; the sharp sword will not cut soft silk. By using sweet words and gentleness you may lead an elephant with an hair.'

In expiation of what had happened they fell at his feet, and after bestowing hypocritical kisses on his hands and face, brought him into the boat and carried him over until they came to a pillar of a Grecian building that stood in the river, when the boatman called out: " The boat is in danger, let one of you who is the strongest and most courageous get upon this pillar and lay hold of the boat's rope, that we may save the vessel." The young man in the vanity of his strength, of which he had boasted, thoughtless of the offended heart of his enemy, paid no attention to this maxim of the sages: " If you have committed an offence towards another, and should afterwards confer a hundred kindnesses, think not that he will forget to retaliate upon thee that single offence; for the arrow may be extracted from the wound, but the sense of injury still rankles in the heart." ' What excellent advice gave Yuktash to Khiltash: If you have scratched your enemy, do not consider yourself safe.' ' When from your hand the heart of another hath suffered injury, expect not to be free from affliction thyself. Fling not a stone against the walls of a castle, lest perchance a stone may be thrown at you from the castle.'

As soon as he had gathered the rope round his arm, and had reached the top of the pillar, the boatman snatched the rope out of his hand and drove the vessel forward. The helpless young man remained astonished. For two days he suffered much distress and underwent great hardship. The third day sleep overpowered him and flung him into the river. After a day and a night he reached shore with some small remains of life. He fed on leaves of trees and roots of grass until he had somewhat recruited his strength, when he bent his course to the desert, and arrived, thirsty and faint, at a well. He saw a number of people gathered round it who were drinking a draught of water at the price of a small piece of money. The young man, having no money, besought them for water, which, they denying, he attempted to obtain by force, but in vain. He knocked some of them down and beat them, but they at length overpowered him, beat him unmercifully and wounded him. 'A swarm of gnats will engage an elephant, notwithstanding all his strength and valour. The little ants, when they meet with an opportunity, will strip off the skin of the fierce lion.'

He fell in with a caravan, which, from necessity, he followed. In the evening they arrived at a place that was infested by robbers. He saw the people of the caravan trembling through fear, and looking as if they expected to die. He said: "Be not afraid, for I am one amongst you who will encounter fifty men, and other men will support me. The

men, encouraged by his boasting, rejoiced at being
in his company, and they supplied him with
victuals and drink. The cravings of the young
man's appetite being very powerful, he ate and
drank so much that at length the inner demon
was quieted, and, being overpowered with fatigue
he fell asleep. An old experienced man, who had
seen the world and was in the caravan, said: " O
companions, I am more afraid of your guard than
of the robbers; for they tell a story of an Arab,
who, having collected together some money,
would not sleep alone in his house for fear of
being robbed by thieves, but got one of his friends
to stay with him from the apprehension he had of
being alone. He stayed with him several nights,
but as soon as he got intelligence of the dirhams,
he seized them and made off. The next morning
they saw the Arab despoiled and lamenting. They
asked: " What can be the matter, excepting that
the thieves may have stolen your money? " He
replied: " By God, not they, but the person who
was the guard." ' I never thought myself secure
with a companion until I knew his disposition.
A wound from the teeth of an enemy is most
severe when it is given under the semblance of
friendship.' How do you know, my friends, but
what this young man may be one of the thieves,
who, by stratagem had introduced himself amongst
us in order that when he finds an opportunity he
may give intelligence to his comrades? My

advice, therefore, is that we leave him asleep and depart."

The advice of the old man was approved by the caravan men, and as they were suspicious of this strong man, they took up their baggage and, leaving him asleep, departed. The young man, when the sun shone on his shoulders, lifted up his head and discovered that the caravan was departed. He wandered about a long time without being able to find the road. Thirsty and without food, he laid his head on the ground in a style of despondency. ' Who will converse with me now that the yellow camels are departed? A traveller has no friend besides a traveller.' ' He is the readiest to distress a traveller who has not himself experienced the difficulties of travelling.' He was uttering this sentence when the king's son, having lost his attendants in pursuit of game, happening to come to the spot, overheard him, and seeing him of good appearance and in distressed circumstances, asked from whence he was, and how he came there. He gave a short account of what had befallen him, and the king's son, compassionating his misery, bestowed on him a garment and money and ordered a trusty person to accompany him and see him safe to his own city.

The father was rejoiced at the sight of him and thanked God for his safe return. At night he related to his father what had happened in the boat, of the violence of the boatman and of the peasants, and the treachery of the caravan. The father said: " O son, did I not tell you at the time of your departure that the strong but poor man has his hand tied, and that his foot, though resembling the paw of a lion, is broken? ' What an excellent saying is that of the needy gladiator: a grain of gold is worth more than fifty pounds of strength.' The son replied: " O father, of a truth, without encountering difficulty you cannot acquire riches, and without you endanger your life you cannot gain the victory over your enemy, and without sowing seed, you cannot fill your barn. Don't you perceive that in return for the little distress that I suffered how much wealth I have brought with me, and for the sting that I endured, what a stock of honey I have acquired?' ' Although we cannot enjoy more than providence has assigned us, we ought not to be negligent in acquiring it.' ' If the diver were to think of the jaw of the crocodile, he would never get in his possession precious pearls.' The lower millstone does not move, and therefore sustains great burdens. ' What food can a ravenous lion find in his den? What game can be taken by a hawk that cannot fly? If you wait in your house for provision, your hands and feet will become as thin as those of a spider.' The father said: " O son, heaven has befriended you this time, and good fortune has been your guide so that you have been able to pluck the rose from the thorn and to extract the thorn from your foot. And a great man met with you, pitied and enriched you and healed your broken condition. But such instances are rare, and from rare instances we cannot formulate a rule. Beware not to loiter about that trap. ' The hunter doth not always carry off the game; perchance himself may one day become the prey of the leopard.' In like manner as happened to one of the kings of Persia, who, possessing a ring set with a valuable jewel, went once on a pleasure party with some of his particular associates to the Musalla-Shiraz and ordered that they should fix the ring on the dome of Azud, with a proclamation that whoever shot an arrow through the circlet of it should have the ring. It chanced there were at that time four hundred experienced archers attending him, whose arrows all missed, but as a boy was playing on the terrace roof of the monastery and shooting his arrows at random, the morning breeze conducted one of them through the ring. The prize was bestowed on him, together with other rich gifts. After this, the boy burnt his bow and arrows, and on their asking him why he had done so, he replied: " That this, my first repute, may be lasting." ' It may happen that the prudent counsel of an enlightened sage does not succeed, and it may chance that an unskilful boy, through mistake, hits the mark with his arrow.'*

* Tale XXVII.

133

ON THE ADVANTAGES OF
TACITURNITY

I HEARD a sage say that no one confesses his own ignorance excepting he who begins speaking whilst another is talking and before the discourse is ended. ' O wise man, a discourse hath a commencement and a conclusion. Confound not one discourse with another. A man of virtue, judgment and prudence speaks not until there is silence.'*

A certain poet went to the chief of a gang of robbers and recited verses in his praise. He ordered him to be stripped of his clothes and expelled the village. The dogs, attacking him in his rear, he wanted to take up some stones, but they were frozen to the ground. Thus distressed, he said: " What a vile set of men are these, who let loose their dogs and fasten their stones." The chief, having heard him from a window, laughed, and said: " O wise man, ask a boon of me." He answered: " I want my own garment, if you will

* Tale VII.

vouchsafe to bestow it. ' A man entertains hopes from those who are virtuous.' I have no expectation from your virtue only do me no injury.' ' We are satisfied with your benevolence in suffering us to depart.'

The chief of the robbers took compassion on him, ordered his garment to be restored, and added to it a robe of fur, together with some dirhams.*

An astrologer entered his own house and, seeing a stranger sitting in company with his wife, abused him, and used such harsh language that a quarrel and strife ensued. A shrewd man, being apprised thereof, said: " ' What do you know of the celestial sphere when you cannot tell who is in your own house? ' "†

A certain person, who performed gratis the office of muezzin in the mosque of Sanjar, had such a voice as disgusted all who heard it. The attendant of the mosque, an amir, a good humane man, being unwilling to offend him, said: " My son, this mosque has muezzins of long standing, each of whom has a monthly stipend of five dinars. Now I will give you ten dinars to go to another place." He agreed to this proposal and went away. Some time after he came to the amir, and said: " O my lord, you injured me by sending

* Tale X.   † Tale XI.

me away from this station for ten dinars; for
where I went they will give me twenty dinars to
remove to another place; to which I have not
consented." The amir laughed and said: " Take
care, do not accept the offer, for they may be
willing to give you fifty. ' No one with a mattock
can so effectually scrape off clay from the face of
a hard stone as your discordant voice harrows up
the soul.' "*

A man with a discordant voice was reading the
Koran aloud when a holy man passing by, asked
what was his monthly stipend. He answered:
" Nothing at all." He resumed: " Why then do
you take so much trouble? " He replied: " I read
for the sake of God." The other rejoined: " For
God's sake do not read. ' If you read the Koran
in this manner, you will destroy the splendour of
Islam.' "†

* Tale XIII.   † Tale XIV.

OF LOVE AND YOUTH

THEY shut up a crow in the same cage as a parrot who, distressed at the other's ugly appearance, was saying: "What is this detestable countenance, this odious form, this cursed object with unpolished manners? Thou crow of the desert, would to God we were as far asunder as the east is from the west. 'Whosoever should behold your face when he is rising, it would convert a goodly morning into a dark evening. Such an ill-fated wretch should have a companion like yourself; but where in the world can your equal be found?'" What is most strange, the crow was equally distressed by the society of the parrot, and, lamenting his fate, complained of the vicissitudes of fortune, and rubbing the claws of sorrow one against the other, was saying: "What ill luck, what mean fate, what a reverse of fortune! It suited my dignity to be strutting on a garden wall in company with another crow. 'It is sufficient imprisonment for a holy man that he should be compelled to associate with profligates.' How far have I sinned that in punishment thereof my life should be spent in company with such a worthless conceited prattler. 'No one will approach a wall on which your portrait is painted. If you had admittance into paradise, everyone would prefer hell to your company.'" I have brought this example to show that howsoever men of understanding may despise the ignorant, these are an hundred times more distressed in the company of the wise.

'A devotee, being at a singing party in company with some profligates, one of the beauties of Balkh said to him: " If you are displeased, do not look sour, for you are bitter enough to us already."' 'In an assemblage of roses and tulips you resemble a dry stick placed in the midst; or like a contrary wind, or intense coldness; or driven snow; or frozen ice.'*

They related to one of the kings of Arabia the story of Layli and Majnún, and the nature of his insanity, that whilst endowed with eminent virtues and possessing uncommon powers of eloquence, he had retired into the desert, abandoned himself to distraction and made his acquaintanceship amongst the beasts. The king ordered him to be brought before him, and when he came, reproachfully asked him what he had seen unworthy in human nature to have induced him to assume the manners of the brutes and to relinquish the

* Tale XII.

pleasures of society. Majnún wept and said: "'Many of my friends reproach me for my love for Layli: will they never behold her charms, that my excuse may be accepted?' 'Would to heaven that they who blame me for my passion could see thy face, O thou ravisher of hearts, that at the sight of thee they might be confounded and inadvertently cut their hands instead of the lemon.' " That the truth of the reality might bear witness to the appearance of what was claimed, the king, being curious to behold her beauty, ordered her to be brought. They searched among the Arabian families and, having found her, brought her before the king in the courtyard of the palace. The king contemplated her appearance and beheld a person of dark complexion and weak form, insomuch that he thought her so contemptible that the meanest servant of his harem surpassed her in beauty and elegance. Majnún, having penetration enough to discover what was passing in the king's mind, said: " O king, the beauty of Layli must be seen through the eyes of Majnún, that the secret of how to behold her may be revealed to you. ' Thou hast no compassion on my disorder, my companion should be affected with the same malady that I might sit all day repeating my tale to him, for two pieces of wood burn together with a brighter flame.' ' The discourse concerning the verdant plain which has reached my ears, had the leaves on that plain heard it, they would have joined

their complaints with mine. Oh, my friends, say to
them who are free from love, Oh, we wish that you
knew what passes in the heart of a lover.'

' The pain of a wound affects not those who are
in health. I will not disclose my grief but to those
who have tasted the same affliction. It were fruit-
less to talk of a hornet to them who never felt
the sting. Whilst thy mind is not affected like
mine, the relation of my sorrow seems only an
idle tale. Compare not my anguish to the cares of
another man; he only has the salt on his hand, but
I have it on the wound in my body.'*

* Tale XVII.

I WAS engaged in a disputation with some learned men in the mosque of Damascus when suddenly a young man, entering the gate, said: " Is there any one amongst you who understands the Persian language? " They pointed to me. I asked what was the matter. He answered: "An old man of a hundred and fifty years of age is in the agonies of death and says something in the Persian language which we do not comprehend. If you will have the goodness to take the trouble to go, you will obtain your reward: perhaps he may want to make his will."

When I came to his pillow, he said: 'I was in hopes that I should have spent the small remnant of my life in ease, but I can scarcely draw my breath. Alas! that at the table of variegated life I ate a little and they said it is enough.' I explained to the Damasciens in Arabic the signification of the discourse. They wondered that at his advanced age he should grieve for worldly life. I then asked him how he found himself. He replied: " What can I say? "

' Have you not seen what pain he suffers who has one of his teeth drawn out of his mouth? Think then what must be the state in that moment when the soul is departing from this precious body.' I said: "Dismiss from your imagination the thoughts of death, and let not apprehension overcome your constitution; for the philosophers have said although the animal system be in full vigour, yet we ought not to rely on its continuance; and, on the other hand, although a disease be dangerous, yet it is no positive proof of approaching death. If you will give me leave, I will send for a physician, that he may prescribe some medicine which may be the means of your recovery." He opened his eyes, laughed, and said: ' The skilful physician smites his hands together when he sees an old fellow fallen. The master of the house is considering how to decorate his hall whilst the foundation is in a state of decay. The sick man was lamenting at his passing whilst an old woman anointed him with a preparation of sandal-wood. When the balance of the temperament is destroyed, neither amulets nor medicines are of any use.'*

In the territory of Diarbekr I was the guest of a very rich old man, who had a handsome son. One night he said: "During my whole life I never had any child but this son. Near this place

* Tale I.

142

is a sacred tree to which men resort to offer up
their petitions. Many nights at the foot of this
tree I besought God, until he bestowed on me
this son." I heard that the son was saying to his
friends in a low tone of voice: " How happy should
I be to know where that tree grows, in order that
I might implore God for the death of my father."
The father was rejoicing in his son's wisdom,
whilst the son despised his father's decrepitude.
' Many years have elapsed since you visited your
father's grave; what piety have you shown towards
your parent that you should expect dutifulness
from your son? '*

* Tale III.

ON THE EFFECTS OF EDUCATION

A CERTAIN vizier had a stupid son whom he sent to a learned man, desiring him to instruct him, in hopes that his capacity might improve. After having instructed him for some time without any effect, he sent a person to the father with this message: "Your son will never find sense and has almost distracted me."

'When nature has given capacity, instruction will make impression, but if iron is not of a proper temper, no polishing will make it good. Wash not a dog in the seven seas, for when he is wetted he will only be dirtier. If the ass that carried Jesus Christ was to be taken to Mecca, at his return he would still be an ass.'*

I saw a schoolmaster in Africa who had a crabbed countenance and a bitter tongue. He was an enemy to humanity, mean spirited and impetuous, so that the sight of him interrupted the pleasure of Moslems, and his reading of the Koran blackened the hearts of men. A number of beauti-

* Tale I.

144

ful boys and tender virgins who were subject to
his tyrannic arm dared not presume to laugh nor
venture to speak, for he used to smite the silver
cheeks of the one, and would sometimes put the
crystal legs of the other into stocks. In short, I
heard that some part of his conduct having been
discovered, they beat him and expelled him, and
gave the school to a pious, good man of so meek
and patient a temper that he never spoke a word
but when he was forced to it, and nothing ever
proceeded from his tongue that could give offence
to anyone. The boys had got the fear of the old
master out of their heads, and seeing the new one
of angelic manners, they behaved wildly towards
one another, and, relying on his forbearance, they
neglected their studies and spent most of their
time in play, and, without finishing their copies,
broke their tablets on one another's heads. ' When
the master is lax in his discipline the boys play at
leap-frog in the market-place.'

A fortnight after I passed by the gate of the
mosque and saw the old master, whom they had
placated and reinstated in his office. In truth I
was concerned, and, invoking God, I said: " Why
have they a second time appointed the devil a
preceptor for angels? " An experienced old man,
hearing me, laughed and said: " Have you not
heard what has been related? ' A king sent his
son to school and placed a silver tablet under his
arm. On the face of the tablet was written in gold:

" The severity of the master is better than the indulgence of the father." '*

I saw an Arab who said to his son: " O my child, in the Day of Resurrection they will ask you what you have done in the world and not from whom are you descended. That is, they will inquire about your virtue and not about your father. ' The cloth that covers the Kaaba and which they kiss is not famous from having been manufactured by the silkworm; it associated some days with one who is venerable, on which account it became venerable like himself.' "†

In the writings of the sages they have related that scorpions are not produced according to the ordinary course of nature, as other creatures, for that they devour the mother's entrails and tear open her belly, and flee to the desert; and the skins which are found in the holes of scorpions give proof of this matter. I mentioned this extra-ordinary circumstance to a wise man, who said: " My heart bears evidence to the truth of this observation, and it cannot be otherwise, for since in their infancy they behaved so towards their parents, therefore they are disapproved and un-beloved in riper age."

' A father exhorted his son, saying: " Young man, store up this lesson in your memory, he who

* Tale IV.   † Tale VIII.

146

is not grateful to those who gave him birth will never be favoured by fortune." ' They asked a scorpion why he did not stir abroad in the winter. He replied: " What reputation have I in summer that I should come again in winter? "*

The wife of a dervish was with child, and the term of pregnancy completed. The dervish, who never yet had a son, said: " If the Almighty will grant me a son I will distribute in charity to the poor all that I possess, excepting the religious habit on my back." It happened that his wife was delivered of a son, at which he rejoiced and made an entertainment for his friends, conformably to his vow. Some years after, when I returned from a journey to Damascus, I passed by the place where the dervish had dwelt, and asked how he went on. They told me he was in the governor's gaol. I asked the reason. They replied: " His son got drunk, had a quarrel and killed a man and fled out of the city, on which account they had put a chain about the father's neck, and heavy fetters on his feet." I said: " His own prayer brought down this misfortune from God. ' O men of understanding, it is better in the opinion of the wise that a woman in labour should bring forth a serpent than wicked children.' "†

On a certain year there happened a quarrel

* Tale IX. † Tale X.

amongst the pilgrims who were going on foot to Mecca, and I was also of that number. Through some act of injustice we fell upon one another's faces, and gave full measure of abuse and blows. I heard one, sitting in a litter, say to his companion: "How wonderful that the ivory pawns in the game of chess, on crossing the whole board, become viziers (or queens), increasing their quality; but that the foot pilgrims to Mecca, after passing the whole desert, are worse than at first." ' Say from me to the hájji who injures and lacerates the skin of his fellow creature, thou art not so true a pilgrim as the poor camel, who feeds on thistles and carries a load.'*

A man, being struck with a pain in his eyes, went to a farrier, desiring him to apply a remedy. The farrier, applying to his eyes what he was used to administer to quadrupeds, the man became blind, upon which he complained to the magistrate. The magistrate said: "Go away, there is no plea for damages, for if this fellow had not been an ass, he would not have applied to the farrier." The application of this story is that whosoever employs an inexperienced person on a weighty matter, besides suffering repentance, will, in the opinion of the wise, be considered of a weak understanding. ' The wise man, of enlightened mind, entrusts not an important business to one

* Tale XII.

of mean abilities. The mat-maker, although a weaver, yet is not employed in the silk manu-factory.'*

I saw the son of a rich man sitting by his father's tomb and disputing with the son of a dervish, saying: "My father's monument is of stone, the inscription is in gold, and the pavement is made of marble tesselated with torquoise-coloured bricks. What is your father's grave but a couple of bricks laid together and sprinkled with a handful of earth?" The son of the dervish, on hearing this, said: "Hold your tongue, for before your father can move himself from under this heavy stone, mine will have arrived at paradise." There is a saying of the Prophet, that to the poor death is a relief. 'The dervish has nothing to leave behind with regret. In like manner, the dervish who bears the burthen of poverty will enter the gate of death lightly loaded, whilst he who lives in affluence, with ease and comfort, will doubtless, on that very account, find death terrible. And, in every view, the captive who is released from con-finement is happier than the nobleman who is taken prisoner.'†

I saw, sitting in a company, a certain person who wore the habit of a dervish but without possessing the disposition of one, and, being

* Tale XIII.   † Tale XVII.

inclined to be querulous, he had opened the book of complaint and began censuring the rich. The discourse was turning on this point, that dervishes have not the means, and the rich men not the inclination to be charitable. ' Those possessed of liberal minds have no command of money, and the wealthy worldlings have no munificence.'

To me, who owe my support to the bounty of the great, this language was not at all grateful. I said: " O my friend, the rich are the revenue of the poor, a store-house for the recluse, the pilgrim's hope and the asylum of travellers. They are the bearers of burdens for the relief of others. Themselves eat only when their dependants and inferiors do so, and the remainder of their bounty is applied to the relief of widows, orphans, aged people, relations and neighbours. ' The rich are charged with pious dedications, the performance of vows, the rites of hospitality, alms, offerings, the manumission of slaves, gifts and sacrifices. By what means can you attain to their power, who can only perform your genuflexions, and even those with a hundred difficulties? ' Whether it is for power in generosity or for strength in a religious prostration, the rich are the better endowed, because they possess wealth made lawful by the bestowal of alms, their garments are clean and their reputation spotless, with minds void of care. For the power to yield obedience to God lies in good meals, the truth of worship in a clean garment. What strength can there be with an empty stomach? What bounty from an empty hand? How can the fettered feet walk, and, from the hungry belly what munificence can be expected? 'He sleeps uneasily at night who knows not how to provide for to-morrow. The ants store up in summer that in winter they may enjoy rest.' Leisure and poverty are not found together, and satisfaction dwelleth not with distress. One is standing up to evening prayers, whilst the other it sitting down wishing for his supper; how can these two be compared together? 'He who possesses wealth is busied in devotion, whilst he who is distressed in his circumstances has a distressed heart.'

"Therefore the worship of the rich is more acceptable, their minds being collected and not distracted, for as they are possessed of the means of subsistence they can turn their whole thoughts to devotion. The Arabians say: 'God defend me from distressful poverty, and from the neighbourhood of him whom I dislike,' and there is a tradition from the Prophet that poverty has a black countenance in both worlds."

My antagonist asked: "Have you not heard that the Prophet said, 'poverty is my glory?'"

I replied: "Be silent, for the Prophet alludes to them who suffer in poverty of spirit with submission to the arrows of destiny, and not those who in a religious garb, sell the scraps which have been given them in charity. ' O loud sounding, empty drum, how will you manage on the march without provisions? If thou art a man, free thyself from worldly avarice, instead of turning in your hand a string of a thousand beads.' A dervish without vital religion will not rest until his poverty ends in blasphemy. He who is in poverty is in danger of blasphemy. Without the command of riches you cannot clothe the naked nor use means for liberating captives. How can such as ourselves attain to their dignity, and what comparison is there between the hand that bestows and that which receives? Do you not perceive that the Almighty revealed to us in the Koran the enjoyments of the dwellers in paradise? For them are appointed fruits in gardens of delight, in order that you may know that he who is intent on gaining a subsistence is excluded from this portion of bliss, and that tranquility of mind requires a fixed income. ' To those who are thirsty, the whole world appears in their dreams a spring of water.' "

At the moment I uttered these words, the dervish's patience being exhausted, he drew the sword of his tongue and, making the steed of his eloquence leap and gallop on to the field of effrontery, he said: " You have exaggerated their praise to such a degree and have talked so extravagantly on the subject that one would suppose them to be the antidote against the venom of poverty and the key of the stores of Providence. But they are a set of proud, arrogant, self-conceited, abominable fellows, insatiable after money and possessions, intoxicated with rank and opulence, who speak not without insolence nor behold anyone but with contempt. The learned they call beggars, and the indigent they treat with obloquy. Proud of their riches, and vain of that dignity of which they think themselves possessed, and vaunting in their superiority, they treat all others as their inferiors. They never think it their duty to look kindly on anyone, ignorant of what the sages have said, that whosoever is inferior to others in piety, although he may exceed them in wealth, though in appearance rich, is in reality a poor man. ' If an empty fellow, on account of his wealth, behaves proudly towards a wise man, reckon such a one an ass, although he be a musk-ox.' "

I said: " Speak not disdainfully of them, as they are the masters of generosity."

He replied: " You speak erroneously, for they are slaves to their money. Of what use are they if they are the clouds of August and do not shower down benefits, or of what advantage if they are the fountain of light and do not shine on anyone, and are mounted on the steed of power without performing any course? They stir not a step in the service of God, and part not with a dirham without distressing you with the obligation. They labour in amassing wealth, preserve it with care and leave it with regret, verifying the saying of the sages that the miser's money comes out of the earth at the time that he goes into it. ' One person by his exertions acquires money which another comes and takes away without pains or trouble.' "

I replied: " You know nothing of the parsimony of the wealthy, excepting by means of beggary; for otherwise whosoever lays aside desires sees no difference between the bountiful man and the miser. The touchstone proves what is gold, and the beggar him who is stingy."

He said: " I speak of them from experience, for they keep a guard at their gate and station rude, violent men to deny admittance to their dearest friends, and these, seizing the collars of men of distinction, declare that nobody is at home; and verily they say truly. He who hath neither wisdom, liberality, prudence nor judgment, of him the porter says rightly that no one is in the house."

I replied: " In this they are excusable, because they are teased out of their lives with importunate solicitations, and tormented with beggarly petitions, and it is a contradiction to reason to suppose that if the sands of the desert were converted into pearls they would satisfy the hopes of beggars. ' The eye of an avaricious man cannot be satisfied with wealth any more than a well can be filled with dew.' You will everywhere see a person who is in distress commit atrocious actions without any hesitation; not being deterred by the dread of future punishment, he discriminates not between lawful and unlawful. ' If a dog is struck on the head with a clod of earth, he jumps up with joy, thinking it to be a bone; and if two persons should carry a corpse on their shoulders, a mean wretch might suppose it a tray of victuals.' But the rich man, whom God hath regarded with the eye of favour, by the performance of what is lawful is preserved from the commission of what is illegal. Since I have made the matter certain by my words and adduced substantial proofs in support of my arguments, I rely on your justice for a decision. Did you ever see an impostor with his hand fastened behind his back, or in prison for lack of means; or the veil of innocence rent, or the hand amputated [for theft] without the plea of poverty? Men, intrepid as lions, are driven by want to undermine men's houses, and are in consequence bound by the heels. And it is possible that the dervish, at the instigation of lust, not having the power to restrain it, may commit sin. ' He who hath in his possession a nymph of paradise, what inclination can he entertain for the damsels of Youghma?' ' He who hath in his hands such dates as he loveth, never thinketh of flinging stones at clusters on the tree.' In general, those in indigent circumstances want chastity, as those who are starving steal bread. ' When a ravenous cur gets meat, he enquires not whether the flesh is of [the prophet] Salih's camel or of the Antichrist's ass.' Many men, naturally well disposed, have been led by poverty into wickedness, and have given their good name to the winds of disrepute. 'Amidst the cravings of hunger, the power of abstaining ceases; poverty snatcheth the reins out of the hand of piety.' Hatim of Tayy was an inhabitant of the desert; had he dwelt in a city he would have been overwhelmed by the importunities of beggars, who would have torn the clothes off his back. As it has been said: 'Look not upon me, that others may not wait in expectation, for from a beggar's hand one can receive no recompense.' "

He said: 'I pity their condition.'

I replied: " Not so, for you envy them their riches."

We were talking thus, opposing force to force, when he advanced a pawn. I endeavoured to repel it, and whenever he put my king in check, I relieved it by the vizier [queen] until he had exhausted all the coin in his purse of effort, and had spent all the arrows of the quiver of disputation. 'Take care not to throw down the shield when combating with an orator who hath nothing but borrowed tumid eloquence. Practise thou religion and serve God, for the verbose orator, who measures his periods, exhibits arms before the gate, but there is nobody inside of his castle.' At length when he had no arguments left I had put him to

shame; he became outrageous, and spoke inco-
herently. It is the way with the ignorant when
confounded by the adversary's arguments, to have
recourse to violence, as Azur, the idol-maker,
when he could not convince his son Abraham by
arguments, began to quarrel, as God hath said:
" Of a truth, if thou wilt not give up this point
I will stone thee." He gave abuse, I retorted
harshly; he tore the collar of my garment and I
laid hold of his beard. ' We were tumbling over
one another and the people running after us,
laughing and astonished at our conduct. Finally,
we referred our case to the cadi, and agreed to
abide by his impartial decision, in order that a
Mahommedan judge might resolve what was
advisable, and discriminate between the rich and
the poor.

When the cadi saw our faces and heard our
discourse, he sunk his chin into the collar of re-
flection, and after mature consideration raised up
his head and said: " O thou who hast spoken in
praise of the rich and hast considered it lawful to
revile the poor, I would have thee to know that
there is no rose without a thorn, and that wine is
accompanied with intoxication. Hidden treasure
has its dragon; in the same place which has royal
pearls are ravenous crocodiles. The enjoyment of
worldly pleasure is followed by the sting of death,
and the lights of paradise are intercepted by crafty
Satan. ' He ought to submit to violence from an

enemy who wishes to enjoy a friend, because the
treasure and the dragon, the rose and the thorn,
sorrow and gladness are linked together.' Observe
you not that in the garden there are musk willows
as well as dry trunks? In like manner in the circle
of rich men there are grateful and ungrateful
persons, and in the number of dervishes some
exercise patience and others do not. ' If every
hailstone were a pearl, the market would be as
full of them as a donkey is covered with beads.'
The beloved of the Almighty consist of rich men
who have the disposition of dervishes, and of
dervishes possessed of noble minds. The greatest
rich man is he who relieves the distress of the
poor, and the best of dervishes is he who looketh
not to the rich for his support, for God hath said:
' He who trusteth in God requires no other's
help.' ''

The cadi, having ceased reprehending me,
turned towards the dervish and said: '' You who
have advanced that the rich spend their time in
wickedness and are intoxicated with luxury, it is
true there are such people as you have described,
who are defective in zeal and ungrateful towards
God; who gather money and hoard it; who enjoy
themselves and give not to others. If, for example,
there should be a drought, or if the world should
suffer a deluge, they, confiding in their own wealth
would not enquire after the distress of the poor,
nor fear God, and would say: ' If another should

be annihilated by lack of means [what matter?];
I have means. What has a goose to fear from a
deluge? The women who are mounted on camels,
feel not in their litters for him who perishes in the
sand.' ' Mean persons, when they have escaped
with their own blanket, say 'what signifies it if
the whole world should die?' There are some of
this description; but I have seen others who,
having spread the table of generosity and proclaimed munificence and girded their loins for
service, with affable countenance seek reputation
and ask pardon of God, enjoying the things of
this world and of futurity; like his majesty, the
king of the world, who is assisted by the grace of
God, the conqueror of his enemies, lord paramount
of nations, defender of the strongholds of Islam,
heir of the kingdom of Solomon, surpassing all
the monarchs of his time in justice, Muzaffaru 'l
Dunyá wa 'l Din, Abu Bakr Sa'd ibn Zangi, may
God prolong his days and grant victory to his
standards! ' A father showeth not such benevolence towards his son as your hand of liberality
has bestowed on the human race. God, waiting
to bestow a blessing on mankind, through his
mercy made you king of the world.' "
When the cadi had extended his discourse to
this length and had exerted the powers of eloquence beyond our expectation, we acquiesced in
his sentence with mutual forgiveness, and apolo-
gising for all that had passed between us, we took

the road of affability, and blaming ourselves, we kissed each other's hands and face and the disputation concluded with these words: " O dervish, complain not of the revolutions of this world, for thou wilt be unhappy if thou expire in this imagination. And thou, rich man, whilst thou hast thy heart and hand at thy command, enjoy and bestow, that thou mayest obtain the blessing of heaven in this life and in futurity."